LESLIE McFARLANE'S HOCKEY STORIES

LESLIE McFARLANE'S
HOCKEY
STORIES

EDITED BY BRIAN McFARLANE

KEY PORTER BOOKS

Library and Archives Canada Cataloguing in Publication

McFarlane, Leslie, 1902–1977
    Leslie McFarlane's Hockey Stories / edited by Brian McFarlane.

ISBN 1-55263-717-4

    1. Hockey stories, Canadian (English) I. McFarlane, Brian, 1931– II. Title.

PS8525.F4T45 2005   jC813'.54   C2005-902769-X

THE CANADA COUNCIL | LE CONSEIL DES ARTS
FOR THE ARTS | DU CANADA
SINCE 1957 | DEPUIS 1957

ONTARIO ARTS COUNCIL
CONSEIL DES ARTS DE L'ONTARIO

The publisher gratefully acknowledges the support of the Canada Council for the Arts and the Ontario Arts Council for its publishing program. We acknowledge the support of the Government of Ontario through the Ontario Media Development Corporation's Ontario Book Initiative.

We acknowledge the financial support of the Government of Canada through the Book Publishing Industry Development Program (BPIDP) for our publishing activities.

Key Porter Books Limited
Six Adelaide Street East, Tenth Floor
Toronto, Ontario
Canada M5C 1H6

www.keyporter.com

Text design and formatting: Ingrid Paulson

Printed and bound in Canada

05 06 07 08 09 5 4 3 2 1

To the author's hockey-playing great-grandchildren:
Kelly, Max and Thomas Jackson,
and Keegan, Samantha and Aubrey McFarlane

CONTENTS

FOREWORD

BACK IN the 1930s, my father Leslie McFarlane made his living as a freelance writer, churning out dozens of stories for Canadian and American magazines on his old Underwood typewriter. During the Depression, he also contracted to write a couple of books in the Hardy Boys series every year under the pen name Franklin W. Dixon. For each book in the series, my father received the princely sum of one hundred dollars, but no royalties. No wonder the McFarlanes never owned a house or even a car! Those books, which many of you read voraciously, have sold in the millions.

Surprisingly, my father took little pride in the Hardy Boys and once admonished me, "Don't tell your friends I'm writing that nonsense." It never seemed to bother him that he, as the ghost writer, made a pittance while the publisher raked in a fortune. However, he did take some pride in his adventure and mystery stories. And even more pride, I believe, in his sports stories—especially those about hockey.

While never much of a player—he was not much bigger than a jockey—my father had always been a knowledgeable hockey fan and once served as a guest colour commentator alongside Foster Hewitt during a 1937 broadcast of a game from Maple Leaf Gardens. It was a role that I would assume on televised games many years later.

In the early thirties, when the editor of an American pulp magazine specializing in sports fiction published a few McFarlane stories about boxing, my father tentatively asked him, "How about letting me try my hand at some hockey fiction?" At first the man threw cold water on the idea. "Who would read it?" he replied. "It's too Canadian. My readers know nothing about hockey."

Apart from a few thousand hockey fans living in or near NHL cities like Boston, Detroit, New York or Chicago, it was assumed most readers of pulp magazines had never seen a big league hockey game. "It would be like trying to sell a baseball story to magazine readers in England," the editor argued. My dad persisted, reminding the editor that a few thousand Canadians read his magazine. The man shrugged and said, "Well, I'll probably get a lot of mail from sports fans asking if I've gone off my nut. But let's try it. Just one story, mind. A short one."

So my dad wrote "Goalie, Keep Your Cool" and the editor gave his stamp of approval. Nobody questioned the man's sanity. In fact, he received a lot of highly favourable mail, most of it from hockey fans who said, in effect, "It's about time you published a story about the world's greatest game. Let's have more." There were also letters from readers who said, "Great stuff. How long has this game been going on?"

From then on that editor printed all the hockey stories Leslie McFarlane could turn out. A few other sports magazines fell into line. Until my dad turned to other work during the war, and began writing and directing movies for the National Film Board (one of his documentaries was nominated for an Academy Award), he sold half a dozen hockey novelettes and short stories every year.

Three bound volumes of these yarns are on my bookshelf today. I treasure them more than the Hardy Boys because, well, because they're about hockey. And hockey has been my life. They were written when I was a little kid, trying out my first pair of skates on frozen ponds and in the Whitby Arena. I longed to grow up and be a star like the young men my dad wrote about.

Soon after he stopped writing his stories about mythical hockey players—among the earliest hockey fiction ever published—the pulp magazines vanished from the scene. Reluctantly, my dad's fictional heroes—"Skates" Kelsey, Bing McGonigal, "Sniper" Jack Parmalee, "Diving" Danny Wade and many others—were forced to hang up their skates. No lucrative pensions, no Hall of Fame inductions, no invites to sports celebrity dinners, or golf tournaments for them. They simply disappeared—until now.

Hockey has changed dramatically over the years. Chicken wire no longer affords a screen behind the goal nets, natural ice is a rarity—if it even exists—in small town rinks, the sixty minute man, and the unmasked goalie have vanished like straight-bladed sticks and the barrels of water used to re-surface the ice before the Zamboni. But the basics remain: the speed, the hard-hitting slam bang combat, the suspense that makes for good drama. I'm confident some of the yarns I've dusted off and edited will still give much pleasure to readers—hopefully as much as they gave to me so many years ago.

—Brian McFarlane

MONTVILLE BOY MAKES GOOD

T HE IDEA, *naturellement*, was conceived in the fertile brain
of Oscar Plouffe. He developed it, rounded it into shape,
perfected it and gave it to Montville in all its beautiful
simplicity.

As a consequence, the engineer gaped from his cab in
bewilderment as the train pulled into Montville that winter
afternoon. For the platform was crowded. Now, the popu-
lation of Montville is not large, but neither is the station
platform; and when every man, woman and child in the village
is apparently seized by a simultaneous impulse to meet the
same train the result is a mob scene of no mean proportions.

"A wedding, perhaps," said the engineer to his fireman as
the train came to a stop.

"But no," exclaimed the fireman a few moments later.
"They are all getting on the train!"

The engineer promptly swallowed his chewing tobacco.
You could not blame him. It was, you comprehend, a veritable exodus.

One might have thought Montville had received word, on the best authority, that the village was marked for destruction by earthquake that very night, and that the good folk were sensibly fleeing from the wrath to come. One might have thought that, I say, had it not been for the hilarity that prevailed. Pushing and scrambling, laughing and chattering, with smiles on their faces and expectation in their eyes, they left Montville as if this departure was the most joyous occasion of their lives.

There was Pierre Labonne, the notary, dignified as a bishop and immaculate as a bridegroom, exhorting everyone to be calm. There was Mayor Lillivert, with his wife and all the little Lilliverts. There were Mademoiselles Celestine, Jeanne and Alphonsine Jolivet. There was the wealthy Hermidas Tessier, and old Grand-père Poupet and Monsieur Doucet, and Aristide Perrault. Nearly everyone was there. Scarcely a handful of people had been left in Montville.

Ah, but this was a proud moment for Oscar Plouffe! It was his idea, and Montville had responded nobly. All, that is, save the bedridden, some of the infants in arms, the town constable and that old skinflint Gabriel Potvin, dealer in hay and feed.

And when the coaches were jammed, when the conductor came out of his daze long enough to sing out, "Bo-oard!"

it was Oscar Plouffe who really gave the engineer his orders. He waved grandly to the popeyed man in the cab.

"Let us proceed!" he boomed.

And they proceeded, with Oscar Plouffe puffing triumphantly as he clambered up the steps. Montville cheered. Montville was going to Montreal.

• • •

UP IN THE smoking car, Oscar Plouffe sat like a plump and benevolent potentate. Never had there been such a crowd on the train. Every seat was occupied. The aisles were crowded. Such chattering, such laughing, such a hubbub of excited conversation you never heard before.

Naturally the conductor was eaten up with curiosity. Inevitably he sought information from Oscar Plouffe. The innkeeper sat there hugging a mysterious parcel. Graciously, he explained the affair to the conductor.

"Montville goes to the hockey match in Montreal."

The conductor was more puzzled than ever.

"Ah, yes," he said. "Canadiens and Boston, eh? But why? I have never known Montville to show such an interest . . ."

"We go to cheer for Adelard Touchette," said Plouffe proudly.

The conductor scratched his head.

"Touchette? Who is Touchette?"

A rumble of indignation in the smoking car. The hard men of Montville were shocked. What a dolt of a conductor. A man of travel—and he had never heard of Touchette.

Old Phileas Trudel spluttered through his whiskers.

"Perhaps, Monsieur Conductor, you have never heard of Les Canadiens?"

"Certainly I have heard of Les Canadiens. But nevertheless . . ."

Oscar Plouffe raised a fat, restraining hand.

"It is because of Touchette," he explained, "that we of Montville prepared this excursion. We took up a subscription, enough to pay all expenses. An affair of the community, you understand. Everything is arranged, to the last penny. Touchette, you understand, is one of us. He was born in Montville. He played hockey on the little rink behind the schoolhouse. He worked in the grocery store of Monsieur Trudel . . ."

"My store!" proclaimed old Phileas, his chest swelling.

"And now," concluded Oscar Plouffe magnificently, "this very night he brings honour to Montville. We go to cheer for him. He achieves fame. Tonight, Monsieur

Conductor, this native son of Montville plays as a substitute on the right wing for Les Canadiens!"

The conductor was properly abashed.

The reason for the unprecedented exodus from Montville was made clear.

A boy who has risen to the dizzy eminence of substitute right wing for Les Canadiens is not to be regarded lightly in the province of Quebec.

• • •

SUCH CONFUSION, such an uproar when they reached the Montreal station, that ancient, red brick monstrosity that was nevertheless so grand to the innocents from Montville. Such excitement! Old Grand-père Poupet was lost within three minutes and the most incredible anxiety prevailed until the short-sighted old gentleman came hobbling hastily out of the ladies' washroom amid a shrill outcry from that sanctuary. Then three of the Jolivet boys, who had gone in search of Grand-père Poupet, were nowhere to be found, and it was not until ten minutes had passed that Oscar Plouffe discovered them outside the station in the middle of a traffic tangle that had sent threescore streetcar motormen, taxi chauffeurs, truck drivers and constables into tears of exasperation. But at last the delegation was rounded up.

Through it all, Oscar Plouffe remained superbly calm. It was magnificent to see his generalship. And then, when he had guided them outside, a grand gesture and *"Voila!"*

There, with horses stamping, bells jangling and fur-coated drivers all in readiness, were twenty sleighs. A score, no less, all ordered in advance by that genius Plouffe. Such a roar of appreciation! How had Oscar Plouffe guessed that many of the ladies had viewed with apprehension the prospect of a journey in a Montreal taxicab? And then the squealing and guffawing and scrambling and crowding as Montville was wedged into twenty sleighs! They will tell you it cannot be done. The answer is that it was done. Oscar Plouffe must have figured it all out by cubic measurement, for the twenty big sleighs held Montville exactly, with one boy bulging precariously over the side.

But there yet remained a final touch. When Oscar Plouffe decided that Montville should do honour to Adelard Touchette, substitute right-wing player for Les Canadiens, he left nothing undone. Climbing into the lead sleigh, he untied the mysterious parcel that he carried. He unfolded the contents and there, before the amazed and admiring eyes of the crowd, he stretched out a tremendous streamer, a veritable banner, with scarlet letters a foot high. It was attached to the sleigh that all the world of Montreal might read the patriotic legend: "Vive Montville!"

A great cheer went up. And then, with a snapping of whips, a musical clamour of sleigh bells, with wails from the babies, yelps from the ladies, giggles from the young girls, shouts from the men, with laughter and shrieks beyond description, the procession moved off.

"To the Forum," ordered Oscar Plouffe, settling back among the fur robes. Caesar would have given the same order with the same air.

"Yes, sir!" said the driver, with respect. He was a burly, hard-bitten man not given to meekness, but he recognized a great man when he saw one.

And Grand-père Poupet waved his cane at the traffic cop on the corner and whooped shrilly: "Vive Montville!"

• • •

NOW, OF ALL THE Montville folk who crowded gaily into the Forum that night, few were more excited than that pretty Mademoiselle Margot Trudel. This eager girl hugged her father's arm and ecstatically awaited the appearance of Adelard Touchette.

You have guessed it, of course!

In the days when young Adelard Touchette played hockey on the rink back of the schoolhouse, in the days when he worked in the grocery store of Phileas Trudel, in those days he was the devoted slave of Margot. He was a snub-nosed, black-haired youngster, and if Margot believed he would be a great man some day it is certain that no one else in Montville shared that belief. A boy-and-girl affair, but make not a joke of that, mesdames et messieurs, for you well know that the first passion of the young has its own delicately flaming beauty. When Adelard Touchette went to play hockey in Quebec he went with the warm kisses of Margot on his lips.

This, then, was a night of nights for the daughter of Phileas Trudel. In mid-season her lover had been summoned from the team in Quebec to replace an injured player of the great Canadiens. He would make his first appearance in the big league. Adelard was to have his opportunity at last.

Small wonder Montville was proud!

Phileas Trudel was telling Grand-père Poupet, who was deaf and wouldn't have listened anyway, that he had always predicted great things for Adelard Touchette.

"The moment he came into my store and said to me, 'Monsieur Trudel, will you give me a job?' I said to myself, 'Here is a lad who will make his mark in the world.' Often, after he had been playing hockey, I would take him aside and say to him, 'Adelard, you do well, but you have still much to learn. Now, when you shoot the puck . . .'" And Phileas droned away, finally digging his elbow into the ribs of Grand-père Poupet. "Was I not right, hey?"

The ancient jumped, looked at him blankly and piped: "Of a certainty, Phileas. Of a certainty. This is a very large rink."

Margot smiled. She was remembering the times her father had predicted that the lazy young villain Touchette would come to no good because he wasted his time playing hockey when he should have been working.

And now the good folk of Montville, in the fine seats procured for them by that master strategist Oscar Plouffe, were making as much noise among themselves as all the rest of the spectators. There had been no little amusement when they came trooping to their seats, and a wave of laughter when that proud banner had been unfolded to reveal its inscription: "Vive Montville!" But the "millionaires"—those doughty, leather-lunged occupants of the cheaper seats—had recognized kindred souls. They had paused for a moment in their chant of "Les Canadiens *sont la*" and burst into a hearty roar of welcome: "Vive Montville!"

And Oscar Plouffe, rising, cupped his hands to his mouth, filled his lungs and bellowed: "Vive Touchette!"

Programs were fluttering like thousands of tiny flags. Touchette? Who was Touchette? A gentleman in a beaver coat appealed to Plouffe across the aisle.

"Pardon, sir, but who is Touchette?"

Plouffe beamed on him.

"A son of Montville, sir. We are his townsfolk. He is playing tonight as a substitute on the right wing, and permit me to tell you, sir, that it will not be long—"

"That is strange," interrupted the gentleman. "I do not find his name on the program."

Oscar Plouffe, who had been too busy to look at the program that was to be a souvenir of an occasion that would shine in the history of Montville, whisked it from his pocket. He looked. He frowned. Then, with a jaunty air, he shrugged.

"It is doubtless a mistake of the printer."

• • •

BUT IT WAS NOT, unfortunately, a mistake of the printer.

When the red-shirted Canadiens skated out onto the ice, Montville let loose a roar of welcome and eagerly scanned the skimming figures, seeking the sturdy Touchette. But in vain.

Touchette was not with the team. He was not on the ice. Montville took refuge in excuses. Touchette was late, Touchette would appear presently. But everyone was puzzled, disappointed, apprehensive. And when the game began, with Adelard Touchette neither on the ice nor on the players' bench, gloom settled down upon the delegation from Montville.

"But what has happened?" demanded Mayor Lillivert. "We come to see Touchette. Where is Touchette?"

"Yes," piped Adolphus Tantivy. "Oscar Plouffe has arranged this excursion at great expense to us all. It is incredible. I am stunned. We are all made to look ridiculous. Where is Touchette? And where, in fact, is Oscar Plouffe?"

Oscar Plouffe had deserted his delegation in this black hour. The game had begun, and Montville regarded it sourly. The rink roared with cheers for the fleet Canadiens, rang with jeers against the redoubtable Boston crew, but there was not so much as a peep out of the glum little group from Montville.

But Oscar Plouffe had gone into action. A little pale, a little shaken, he was tugging at the elbow of a bored young man in the press box.

"Sir—I beg your pardon—a little information—it is about Touchette—Adelard Touchette—is he ill?"

The bored young man looked at him.

"I'll tell the world," he said. "He's about the sickest kid in Montreal right now."

"Is it—is it serious?" spluttered Plouffe.

"Well, they're sending him back to Quebec for a rest. Then he may be ready to take on the heavyweight champ."

The bored young man looked languid and jotted a note on a pad as Morenz streaked down the ice like a hawk from the skies, split the defence, drew out the Boston goalie and slammed the puck into the net. The Forum exploded. After a while Plouffe was able to make himself heard.

"Rest? Heavyweight champ?"

"You'll find Touchette in the dressing room. He socked the coach on the nose before he ever got a workout. I think he's a mental case myself. Goofy as a gopher."

This, as the ghastly truth sank in, was probably the blackest moment of Oscar Plouffe's life. He had organized this excursion, he had brought the people of Montville a hundred miles to Montreal—and Touchette was not to play for the Canadiens after all. The young dolt had socked the coach on the nose and was to be sent back in disgrace! The great excursion had been for nothing.

"We shall see," muttered Plouffe.

Doors never remain closed to Oscar Plouffe. How he obtained access to the dressing room, there to confront the wretched Touchette who sat in lonesome misery beside a water bucket, how he learned the story of Touchette's downfall is a matter best known to himself.

"It was a joke, Monsieur Plouffe," muttered the culprit. "I have been a fool. I am ruined."

"A joke? You struck the coach on the nose as a joke? You have a strange sense of humour," said Plouffe grimly.

"They play jokes on most young fellows when they join the team," explained Touchette. He was more rugged, more thickset than Plouffe had remembered him. "The players said to me: 'Be on your guard against a big fellow who will try to make a fool of you. It is his practice to tell new men that he is the coach and to give them orders. Pay no attention to him. He is merely a loafer who has nothing to do with us.' So I resolved that this loafer would not make a fool of me. When he came into the dressing room and said 'Do this' and 'Do that,' I said, 'No, you big loafer, I shall take no advice from you.' And what with one word leading to the next one, we both became excited and I hit him on the nose." Touchette groaned. "And he *was* the coach after all."

Plouffe shook his head thoughtfully as he regarded the despairing Touchette.

"There are more than a million people," he observed, "on the Island of Montreal. With so many to choose from—if you must hit people on the nose—bah! Well, it is necessary that there be action immediately. Montville must not be disappointed."

And he hustled away.

• • •

THE FIRST PERIOD was over, the Canadiens were leading by two goals, the loudspeakers were belching sweet music, the Forum was echoing with the great hollow roar of the crowd, and the citizens of Montville were muttering with wrath.

"Where," demanded Adolphus Tantivy for the nineteenth time, "is Oscar Plouffe? He has made fools of us. Certainly an explanation is owing."

"Such an expense, this journey," growled Monsieur Tessier. "One can imagine how the people of Champeau will laugh when they hear of this."

Mayor Lillivert winced. The rival town of Champeau would never permit this catastrophe to be forgotten.

"One envies Gabriel Potvin," he said. "He had sufficient intelligence to remain at home and hear the game by radio, at no cost whatever."

As for Margot Trudel, she was trying to pretend that she had a cinder in her eye. The poor child was heartbroken.

Down in the office of the management of the Canadiens, the worthy Plouffe was under full steam. A fortunate meeting with an executive of a brewery with which the Hotel Vendôme did business had done the trick. An introduction in the right place, and now Plouffe was battling right nobly for Touchette, for Montville.

"I have brought nearly two hundred people to this game. We have travelled a hundred miles. The affair has been managed at great expense, for we are not wealthy folk. We are assured by the newspapers that Touchette will play. And now we are disappointed. Gentlemen, I appeal to you, for the sake of my friends. If any of you come from a small town you will realize our emotions. As for Touchette, he assures me it was a mistake. He wishes to apologize . . ."

The coach, who was present, waved a negligent hand.

"That's all right," he said. "One of the boys told me all about it. They were ribbing the kid. I should have gotten wise. But you see, Monsieur Plouffe, he took a poke at me. That's bad for discipline. Now, as a matter of fact, the kid isn't being sent back to the minors. We couldn't let him play tonight, but that was to throw a scare into him, teach him a lesson . . ."

"But the punishment," said Plouffe, "falls upon these good people who have paid for their seats and travelled a hundred miles. The boy has had his lesson, I assure you. What harm will there be, when your team is already leading by two goals, to permit him to play for a little while? Gentlemen, on behalf of Montville . . ."

• • •

OSCAR PLOUFFE can be very compelling at times. It is generally agreed in Montville that the hotel profession's gain was the legal profession's loss when Plouffe chose his life work.

Shortly before the beginning of the second period he puffed his way down the aisle, back to his seat among the melancholy folk of Montville. But Plouffe was not melancholy. His florid face glowed with triumph.

"Monsieur Plouffe," yelped Adolphus Tantivy, "we have been waiting for an explanation. You have brought us here at great expense, on your solemn promise that Adelard Touchette would appear tonight with Les Canadiens. It is outrageous ..."

"Monsieur Tantivy," said Plouffe calmly, "my promise is never broken. Touchette will play. I have arranged it."

Montville gasped. Margot Trudel sat up, eyes shining, cheeks glowing. Grand-père Poupet uttered a shrill cheer. Clamour broke forth.

What a man!

And now the second period got under way. Sticks clashed, the players skimmed over the ice sheet like swallows, the crowd howled, goalies leaped and slid, the puck sped hither and thither, men crashed to the ice. Boston attacked furiously, the Canadiens defended their net stoutly. And at last, during an offside face-off, when three of the Canadiens trudged off the ice for a rest, a sturdy youth in a red sweater leaped eagerly out onto the ice and skated over to his position at right wing.

The great banner was raised on high.

"Vive Montville!" they roared.

Grand-père Poupet brandished his cane.

"Vive Touchette!" bellowed Oscar Plouffe. It was a small sea of sheer bedlam. And as those doughty "millionaires" realized the situation, they rose to their feet and welcomed the newcomer with a roar.

"Vive Touchette!"

Margot Trudel flung her arms about her father's neck, half strangling him, and wept with excitement and joy.

"Let go! Let go, *ma petite*!" he begged. "They are playing. I cannot see."

Great was Montville's pride in that glorious moment as young Adelard Touchette took his place with the elite of the hockey world. And, as the puck was faced off, young Touchette beamed with pleasure. He waved toward his townsfolk, eagerly he sought the pretty face of Margot Trudel.

• • •

WHAM!

The puck dropped to the ice. The centres battled for it, the disc flew across to the grinning Touchette's feet and found him all unprepared. A Boston forward swept in with the speed of a runaway locomotive. Touchette woke up, made a feeble stab at the spinning rubber, missed, danced wildly for a second, and then sat squarely and ingloriously upon the ice.

A more inglorious debut could not be imagined!

And how the crowd laughed. There was a veritable thunderclap of mirth. That little stepdance of Touchette's, terminating in his undignified downfall, could not have been bettered by the most acrobatic comedian of the movies. Coming so close upon his great reception, it had the essential virtue of contrast. It was sublime. It sent the mob into hysterics. They choked, they yelled, they wept, they laughed.

The laughter, however, was mercifully brief. For the Boston forward who had made Touchette look so ridiculous had sailed in, to make the Montreal goaltender jump like a jack rabbit to block a burning drive. And in the next instant the Boston forwards were buzzing around the cage. The Canadiens, perhaps a little shaken, a little upset by Touchette's humiliation and the unholy explosion of laughter, were forced back. Players were piled in a heap around the net. The red light flashed.

A Boston goal!

Oscar Plouffe sat down, breathing heavily. He felt ill. All Montville felt ill. All except Grand-père Poupet, who stood and cheered, under the impression that Touchette had inaugurated his big-league career by scoring a goal against Boston. No one took the trouble to enlighten him.

"Well," sighed Plouffe hopefully, "perhaps he will do better next time."

But Touchette did not do better next time. Not satisfied with making himself ridiculous before thousands of people, that miserable youth skittishly proceeded to humiliate Montville.

Many rookies had passed through the hands of the coach, and he did not bench Touchette instantly. He would give the boy a chance, but the temperament of Adelard Touchette was of a sensitive nature. Laughter, ridicule, the terrible knowledge that he was to blame for that Boston goal shattered his confidence, broke his morale, left him a shivering wreck.

Stage fright!

He took a pass at his own blue line and stumbled away with the puck. He faltered, lost the disc, regained it, plunged on down the ice until he met the oncoming Boston wing. Touchette was rattled. He should have passed the puck to his uncovered centre. He tried to evade the wing, clumsily. The puck was taken from him and another Boston rush was on. The Boston forward was sent flying on his ear at the defence, but that didn't help Touchette.

Again, the Canadiens took advantage of a penalty to launch an attack. They swarmed back to the Boston blue line. Touchette plunged valiantly and foolishly into a mob of struggling players, and emerged like a disorderly customer from a tavern. He picked himself up from the ice out in front of the Boston goal and then—miracle of miracles—the puck came skimming out of the crowd.

It clicked smartly against his stick. The goalie was lying sprawled in the net. The pride of Montville gaped. He looked at the puck, he looked at the goal. The crowd shrieked.

In the nick of time, with two Boston players plunging toward him, with the goalie scrambling desperately to his feet, Touchette realized that destiny had presented him with the opportunity of a lifetime. Hastily he shot—skied the puck ten feet over the net into the back screen!

Oscar Plouffe, utterly crushed, buried his face in his hands.

Margot Trudel wept openly.

Montville groaned unanimously.

The cheers of the crowd changed to howls of exasperation.

Touchette was benched.

And Oscar Plouffe, with bent shoulders, muttered desolately to himself: "I shall never live this down—no, not in three hundred years."

A few minutes later Boston tied the score. The name of Adelard Touchette was mud and there was hissing in the Forum. People looked at the delegation from Montville as if to say, "So this is the breed that produces such unspeakable dolts as that Touchette!" No one dared fold up that once-proud banner, but everyone wished heartily that the thing was out of sight.

At the end of the second period Oscar Plouffe disappeared very rapidly.

• • •

THEY HAD PAID for their seats, and the train did not leave until midnight in any case, so the delegation from Montville remained for the third period. But if ever an excursion party radiated dejection, it was that gloomy group. They came, they saw, they were humiliated. They were not cheered by certain ribald enquiries from humorous folk wanting to know if Montville had other natural resources aside from hockey players.

What did it matter to Montville that the Forum had not seen such hockey all season as the hockey that raged in that final period? Boston had come from behind to tie the score, and the teams battled furiously to break the deadlock. Swift, stirring rushes down the ice, grim, hard-fought defensive play, crashing bodychecks, electrifying scrambles around the nets—the period hit a terrific pace from the outset. The Montville folk regarded the spectacle without enthusiasm.

Oscar Plouffe, his fat face a little anxious but by no means as gloomy as the occasion warranted, sat beside Margot Trudel. He patted her shoulder.

"There is yet a chance," he said, consoling her. "I had a little talk with our young friend. And with the coach. He is not a bad fellow, that coach. Perhaps even yet . . ."

But the minutes went on. The teams played themselves into exhaustion. The score remained tied. Adelard Touchette remained on the bench. Adolphus Tantivy audibly expressed the opinion that he would do well to crawl under it.

And then, suddenly, the miracle! With two of his players suffering injuries, with others sagging with exhaustion, the coach gave Touchette another chance. With five minutes to go, he leaped out onto the ice, his jaw set, his mouth grim, without a glance at the crowd. No, there was no stage fright about Touchette now. He had eyes for only one man in the rink and that man was the Boston goalkeeper.

• • •

MONTVILLE GASPED. Montville surged with new hope. Montville saw Touchette take a pass, they saw him heading madly toward the Boston net. Fresh and eager, deaf to the roars of the crowd, he sped to the blue line like a whirlwind, evading his weary check, racing in on the Boston defence. He headed toward the goal as if the defence did not exist. A burly defender stepped squarely in his path. Down went Touchette, spread-eagled on the ice. Up he came again, whirled, raced into a corner and stole the puck from under the very nose of a Boston player. Out he came again, doggedly, with one purpose in his mind. He sidestepped, swooped in ... he shot!

• • •

PITY THE BOSTON GOALIE. No one could have followed the course of that puck. No one could have seen it. One cannot see a bullet in flight. Fortunate indeed for the goalkeeper that he jumped the wrong way in a foolhardy attempt to stop that terrific drive, for the puck would assuredly have gone right through him.

But, yes! Do you not understand? Touchette scored.

Not only that, but, while the rink was still thunderous with acclaim, while the good folks of Montville were shrieking deliriously, while the game had still a minute to go, he took the puck from back of the Canadiens net, raced down the ice at 190 miles an hour, split the defence and let loose another of those wicked, those incredible shots that seemed impelled by a howitzer rather than by human arms and wrists—a shot that would have knocked the goalie's head right off his shoulders if it had not, fortunately, missed him and whizzed into the net. Ah, magnificent was Touchette! The crowd turned a collective back somersault, drew in its breath and then let loose a spontaneous roar of joy that was heard—one understands on excellent authority—as far away as Dominion Square.

And, blandly smiling upon the mob of howling maniacs that had once been a dejected delegation from Montville, with Margot Trudel clinging to his neck, with Grand-père Poupet pounding somebody's bowler hat into wreckage with his cane—blandly, smiling, I say, stood Oscar Plouffe.

For it was Oscar Plouffe, you must understand, who had made this triumph possible. A great psychologist, that Plouffe! A man of deep understanding and infinite resource. Stage fright? There is a cure for that. Give the victim something else to think about. But Oscar Plouffe's part in that affair was not realized until some time afterward, when Adelard Touchette, the hero of the hour, came striding up to his admiring townsfolk. He paid scant attention to their vociferous acclaim. Grimly, he sought out pretty Margot Trudel.

"Now," he said fiercely, "perhaps you will cheer for him again."

Margot stared at him, uncomprehending.

"Cheer for him? For whom, Adelard?"

"For that Boston goalkeeper."

"But I do not understand," faltered Margot. "Never did I cheer for him ..."

"I know all!" declared Touchette dramatically. "When Monsieur Plouffe came to me at the end of the second period and told me that the people of Montville were disappointed in me, I said to him: 'And Margot—is she disappointed, too?' He laughed. 'You have not heard, then?' he said. 'You have not heard that the Boston goalkeeper spent the summer near Montville? Of all your old friends, she is the only one who tonight cheers for Boston.'"

Touchette glared at her.

"So you would cheer for him, ha?" he said. "You have wasted your breath tonight, my fine young lady."

Margot gasped.

"But Adelard! The Boston goalkeeper—I do not know his name. I never saw him in my life! Why, Monsieur Plouffe himself can tell you . . ."

But Oscar Plouffe had discreetly disappeared.

GOALIE GARRISON'S GOAT

I **COULD SEE** that the kid was keyed up. His fingers were all thumbs and his hands were shaking so he could scarcely buckle on his pads. We were all keyed up for that matter.

The Memorial Cup, junior championship of the world, just one game within reach, and I knew we had the scoring punch to grab it. I wasn't worrying about the rest of the Indian team. They would settle down when they felt ice under their skates. But if your goalie has the jitters, anything can happen.

"Well, boy, I guess tonight's the night we finish this up, huh?" I said, and slapped young Tub Garrison on the knee.

"Tonight's the night, Casey," Tub managed, in a cracked voice.

He knew that the Cup meant more to me than to anyone on the team. Those kids, they had their hockey careers ahead of them. Big-league timber, every boy from goal out. But I had been managing amateur squads for fifteen years and never a title to show for it. If we didn't win this time, yours truly Casey Hearne would be just about washed up.

"Look, kid," I said to Tub. "We've taken two games from these Cubs and dropped one. All we need is one more. Forget that game we lost. Any team that gets into the Memorial Cup finals is due to win one game. Now you settle down and square away and go out there and play the game of your life tonight."

Putting it that way made him feel better. I knew and everybody else knew and especially he knew himself that the Cubs hadn't even been due to take that one game from my Indians.

Tub Garrison had kicked it away because he let the crowd get his goat. But that was all over and I figured he had learned his lesson. If Tub Garrison went out there and forgot about the crowd and played his usual game in goal, we were as good as in.

"I've seen lots of crowds, kid," I told him, "and there ain't no better way of shuttin' 'em up than by shuttin' out the team they're hollering for."

I stood up then. No use saying any more. The rest of the boys were standing around the dressing room, pretty quiet, all ready to go. A fine bunch of players, these Indians. Hy Lennox, that poker-faced little phantom at centre; Big Boy

Krueger and Tim Blake, hardest-hitting defence pair I had ever handled. Comet Adams and Bill O'Day, my wings—oh, a sweet outfit!

And three smart backcheckers for the second-string forward line, a defence spare that wasn't far behind the regulars and sandy-haired young Tub Garrison for goal.

"Let's go, fellows," I said. "We're gonna take 'em tonight, and no foolin'!"

No pep talk. If they weren't ready now, they'd never be ready. So they trooped out of the dressing room, with its warm smell of steam heat and rubbing alcohol and leather and orange peel. I took another glance at Tub Garrison, and I saw that his face was white. I was worried about him.

The Stanley Cup grind is tough, but don't let anybody kid you that the Memorial Cup trail is any cinch. It's a heavy schedule, eliminations all the way, and by the time you hit the finals, your kids have played as many games as a big-league pro team would play in a regular schedule. And they're only kids, high-strung and unseasoned.

Take a youngster like this Tub Garrison, see. The whole strain is on the goalie. If he breaks, it doesn't do any good if the team out in front of him is the best in the world. A hockey squad is just as good as the boy in the hemp cage and no better.

A defenceman can turn in a sour game, a forward can ease up a little and maybe the team will come through anyhow. But let the goalie get a bad one out of his system and what happens? It's marked down as a loss.

Take this kid, Garrison, fresh out of school, and heave him into the Memorial Cup grind with its jammed-up schedule in March, against the best teams in the West. Put him through that grind and then bring him East; put him out there before bigger crowds than he has ever seen in his life—rabid, wild-eyed homers pulling for the Eastern team to win.

If he can remain cool under all that, he's got the makings; if he cracks a little, he's only human.

• • •

THE CROWD JUMPED HIM the minute he skated out. They were waiting for him, laying for him, see! They had rattled him in that other game—rattled him so badly that he had blown sky-high and muffed three soft shots.

He had stepped out of his net and shaken his stick at the mob behind the back screen. And that's bad. Now they knew our weakness, and that crowd was ready to go to town on it.

Tub Garrison didn't even look up. If he had looked them over, or grinned or waved his hand or even thumbed his nose at them, I'd have felt better. But he kept his head down and they razzed him and jeered him, called him everything in the book. Did you ever have twelve thousand people telling you that you were a louse and a no-good bum, all at the same time? It's not music.

He went up to mid-ice for the instructions, then skated back to the north-end net, his head still down. Then he crouched, gripping the old war club as the puck fell and the ref sent the boys on their way.

I'll admit my own heart was pounding in double-quick time.

If we took this game, we'd win the Cup. If we dropped it, the series would be tied at two–all. And if we dropped it because our goalie went sour on us the second time in a row—well, then we'd be as good as washed up. That was why I couldn't take my eyes off Tub Garrison.

It started out as a typical Memorial Cup game. By that I mean that it went into high gear from the drop of the puck and stayed there.

Blinding speed, dazzling skating, slam-bang checking and smart plays. Give me the juniors every time, for action. They've got youth; they've got the legs; they don't save themselves. What game drew the biggest crowd in Canadian hockey history? A Stanley Cup playoff, you think? Nope! It was a Memorial Cup final, and I've given you the answer.

After five minutes I settled back, breathing a little easier. The Cubs had made only one threat on Tub Garrison's goal—a three-man rush that split the defence and left their scoring ace, Amby Doran, in the clear for a pass from the corner.

But Tub Garrison, with that crowd shrieking like lunatics at his back, made Doran shoot for the open corner and picked it off as smart and as cool as you please, cleared to Bill O'Day and set off an Indian rush that sent the play to Cub territory quicker'n you could snap your fingers.

"Ah!" I grunted to Sam Stegg, our trainer. "That's better. The kid is back on the job again."

Stegg merely chewed at the ends of his mustache. He was the sort of guy who always expects the worst.

"The game ain't over yet," he growled.

"It's as good as over, now that I'm sure of Garrison," I cracked.

• • •

AND AS THE PERIOD went on, I was surer than ever. Big Boy Krueger drew himself a penalty at the fifteen-minute mark when the Cubs had their second stringers out, and the first-string forwards came on the ice all rested up for a ganging act.

And how they could gang!

Those Cubs had made the finals on scoring punch. They lit out after that goal now like a crew of maniacs. With the odd-man advantage they backed my lads clean into the end boards. They swarmed around our net like wasps. They shot and they kept on shooting.

Tub Garrison met 'em halfway. He bobbed around in the net like a squirrel in a cage. He kicked out low drives for the corners. He banged out high ones with stick and glove. Half a dozen times, he went down on the goal line with the puck hugged to his chest and Cubs all over him, trying to shove him back into the cage with the puck in his glove.

But he kept that puck out. He tended goal like he'd tended it in the West when we were on our way up. I chewed two cigars into fine cut watching him work, but he made stops that were just plain miracles. Finally, the team steadied down in front of him and got in a little checking to give him protection. Then they got a breakaway just before Big Boy got back on the ice, and Hy Lennox sailed up alone to catch their one-man defence flat-footed and sifted in a counter.

Boy, that big 1 on the scoreboard looked pretty!

"We're in, Sam," I said to Stegg. "We got something to work on now."

And even Stegg got off a grin. Usually it took a five-goal lead to coax a smile out of him.

Tub Garrison had taken the best the Cubs had to offer, had taken everything the crowd could hand him, and he had come through like a thoroughbred. That ended my worries.

When the period ended, with that one-goal lead looking bigger'n Pikes Peak, I was composing the speech I would make when they presented the Cup. I would tell 'em that any coach could have won the title with the team I had.

And so we sailed through the second period. Shutting 'em out. Big Boy Krueger made up for that penalty by going out and snagging himself a goal on a short pass from Comet Adams after they'd teamed up on an end-to-end rush.

And don't think we were having it all our own way. Those Cubs gave me heart spasms many a time with their smart plays that would carry them right up to the crease, shaking off their checks and working in close for their shots—hard shots, tricky shots. Scrimmages right in the goal mouth with nobody knowing where the puck had gone—nobody but Tub Garrison.

And so we came to within one period of the title.

"You're doin' well, kid," I told Tub in the dressing room. "Keep it up. They'll shoot the works in this frame."

The Cubs were on the spot now. They would have to gamble. Trailing by two goals, they would have to go gunning in the next twenty minutes. They had to take the chances. And if my Indians had a specialty, it was cashing in on breakaways when the other team had to carry the play. I saw my lads making a runaway of that last period.

• • •

THE CROWD WAS quieter when we got under way again. They didn't have much to cheer about. The back-screen mob behind Tub Garrison kept riding him, but they were beginning to lose heart.

As the period went on and my boys laid back and made the Cubs come to 'em, checked 'em into the ice without a smell of a goal, the gloom got so thick you could have weighed it out and wrapped it up by the pound.

Then it happened—a Cub rush, a hard shot on goal, a save by Tub, a scramble in the corner.

Everybody was pushing and shoving and batting at the puck. It came skitting out, a bad pass that hit somebody's stick and got deflected. Out it came, rolling, and spun to a stop out in front of the crease. Just too far out for Tub Garrison to reach it with his stick. But in an awfully dangerous spot if a Cub got to it first.

Tub took a chance. He came out for it and just then Amby Doran came whirling around the far corner of the cage, trying to beat Hy Lennox to it from the other side. Tub scrambled back into his net, but he didn't have time to get set before Doran collared the puck and let fly.

It was a bad shot. Doran had just lashed out and golfed it. The puck would have missed the goal post by inches if Tub had left it alone. But he was so busy scrambling back into his net and trying to get set for the stop that he had no time to judge it. His big war club swung out at the rubber.

And he hit it! The puck swerved down to the ice, bounced high and caromed over his boot into the net.

Fluke! A goalie's goal.

Well, these things happen. A goalie with two or three hundred games under his belt would have said to himself: "It's gone into the records, so forget it."

But not Tub Garrison.

The crowd jumped him. They began to clap, figuring he had blown. Have you ever heard twelve thousand people going *clap-clap-clap* in slow time? It's one of the most monotonous and nerve-racking sounds in the world. I could see Garrison glance up over his shoulder as he grabbed one of the goal posts and awaited the next rush after the face-off. That was a bad sign.

The Cubs swarmed in, every man up but the goalie. One little break and it was a clear road up the ice for any of my forwards who could get loose. But we didn't get that break. Carruthers, their left winger, picked up a short pass inside the blue line, shook off Bill O'Day and fired from twenty feet out.

Garrison made the stop. But he was jittery and nervous. He fumbled in clearing. The puck bounced out just beyond the crease, with Carruthers racing in for a slap at his own rebound.

• • •

ORDINARILY, TUB GARRISON wouldn't come out of his net. This time he did. He dived for it, but he was a split second too late. Carruthers hooked it out from under him and let drive just as Krueger barged into him.

Carruthers went down, but the puck went in and away went our lead, blown to smithereens in thirty seconds.

Then the crowd really went to work. And Tub Garrison went to pieces. He didn't even have sense enough to stall, to fiddle with his belly pad or tighten up his pads. Hy Lennox did, trying to give him a chance to settle down, and the crowd went on with that horrible *clap-clap-clap* that shattered every bit of nerve Garrison had left.

It affected the whole team—not the clapping, but the fact that Garrison had blown up. Once a team loses confidence in the goalie, look out! The defence began backing in close and when the Cubs smashed in again, the players were bunched all over the defensive zone. They weren't even looking for breakaway chances now; they were just trying to protect their goal, and praying for overtime.

But they never got it. The Cubs combined on a neat three-man rush that brought them right in on the doorstep. Garrison made one stop, batted the puck wildly out right to Amby Doran's stick, and Doran picked the open side, banged it home with five minutes to go. Three minutes later, they bagged another goal on a breakaway when I sent the whole team up trying to get back the equalizer.

When we trooped back into the dressing room, we were still a game away from the Cup, the series was sewed up, and Tub Garrison was in such a state that when he tried to take a drink of water he let the glass fall out of his hands.

Was I blue?

"We can't beat 'em without a goalkeeper!" yelled Hy Lennox savagely, his nerves getting him as soon as he got inside the door.

"Shut up!" I said.

Tub Garrison sat in a corner with his head down. None of the others spoke to him. And I wouldn't have given a wooden nickel for our chances of taking that rubber game.

• • •

ONE OF THE SPORTSWRITERS was kidding me next day. "Well, Casey," he said, "you'll soon be going back West without the Cup and getting ready for next season. You'll need a new goalie—one who can take it. And I'm gonna tell you where to find him. Run out to Harperstown tonight and catch the County League junior final."

"It'd be a nice holiday for me, seein' a hockey game," I said.

"I'm not kidding. Stratham Bears have a kid named Temple in goal. He's only eighteen, and if you think you've seen tough crowds ride the visiting firemen, wait until you see that Harperstown mob in action."

I figured maybe the trip might do me good. I had been hanging around the hotel for a week and it was getting me down.

So that evening I decided to go out to Harperstown, thirty minutes by bus, and have a peek at this Temple wonder. Maybe we could use him next season at that.

Then I had another idea. I'd take Garrison with me. It wasn't any fun for him, hanging around the hotel with the rest of the team. They hadn't been riding him. They'd just been leaving him alone, which was maybe worse.

• • •

"COME ON, SON," I said to him. "We're going to a hockey game tonight just for a change."

He was grateful. All the way out to Harperstown I talked about anything but hockey, and he seemed grateful for that, too.

Maybe the Memorial Cup series was important to us. But it wasn't any more important than that County League title was to Stratham and Harperstown. They had a smart rink, artificial ice and all, and it was packed with positively the most rabid collection of hockey bugs I had ever listened to in thirty years of the game.

It was a long-standing feud, is what I mean. And when the Bears, the Stratham team, skated out for their warm-up, Tub Garrison was popeyed at the way the hometown crowd went for the visitors.

Twelve thousand people in the Garden couldn't have thought up half the insults those Harperstown fans hurled at the Bears. It was wild. They stormed and booed and yelled, just getting tuned up. Even before the game started, a fan hopped over the rail and took a pass at a Bear forward. He got thrown out on his ear by a cop, but it was just a notion of what was to come.

"Gosh!" said Garrison. "If this is the way they act before the game gets under way, what'll happen if the Bears win?"

I was wondering that, too. It was a long time since I had seen a real, old-time, small-town hockey feud, and it seemed to have a few extra trimmings added since my day.

• • •

I KEPT MY EYE on Goalie Temple. He was a lanky, sad-looking kid, a dreamy bird who just chewed gum and went through his workout as if he was out on a pond fifty miles away from any crowd. And when the game got under way, a real, bang-up, no-holds-barred riot, the sad-faced Temple did his stuff as if that crowd just wasn't in the rink at all.

He wasn't as good as Tub Garrison; a long way from being as good. He could stop 'em all right, but his clearing was a shade slow and he wasn't quick on the trigger in passing the puck out to the right teammate at the blue line. But the big thing was his coolness.

The hometown fans outnumbered the visiting supporters twenty to one, and the art of riding a Stratham hockey team had evidently been handed down from generation to generation. Poker-faced Temple didn't even blink.

They went into the second period scoreless, and Stratham snagged a goal at the halfway mark. The home crowd really did open up then. They began throwing things. It was artistic, just plain artistic, to see Temple stop a frozen tomato with his stick and a flying puck with his skate at the same instant.

I stole a look at Tub Garrison. He was sitting there with his mouth open and the expression on his face might have been hero worship.

"Boy!" I said to myself. "Maybe this will do some good."

The Bears grabbed another goal at the start of the third period, and from then on, the game was spotty. They had to hold it up every five minutes to clear the ice. And going down the last period stretch, the Harperstown team went all out, sending down a five-man attack.

With the crowd yelling like a million maniacs, Harperstown waded in and rained rubber on Temple. He kept on chewing gum and stopping 'em. And in one of these melees, a Harperstown fan pulled a specialty.

Just when Temple was kicking 'em out from all angles, with his defence crumbling in front of him and the opposition all around him, over the back screen came a big red cylinder, spluttering and sizzling.

A firecracker!

Bang!

Off it went, right behind Temple as he was lunging to block a hard low shot from the side.

And, so help me, he didn't even quiver. He made the stop, cleared to the corner and never so much as looked around. It hadn't been a small firecracker either. If you hadn't seen it, you'd have thought somebody in the crowd was lending the hometown team a hand with a double-barrelled shotgun.

"Well," I said to myself, "after that, I've seen everything."

Tub Garrison looked at me. "Holy cats!" said Tub piously. "And he never even looked to see what it was!"

• • •

HARPERSTOWN SWARMED in again, still making it tough for Temple. And right in the heat of it, while he's trying to outguess a forward waltzing in, with the centre getting in position to take a short pass, over came another cannon cracker.

Boom!

Any normal person would have jumped out of his pants, would have been thrown off balance for a fraction of a second just as the pass went over to the Harperstown centre. Not Temple. His right leg went out and he blocked that drive just as it was heading for daylight inside the left goal post.

And then, somebody socked the fellow who had heaved the cannon crackers, and somebody else socked him, and down came the back screen with about a dozen battling fans tumbling out over the ice.

Temple didn't look around. He stopped another shot before the referee blew the whistle.

Well, after all! You can't beat that sort of goalkeeping. The Bears won and got out of the rink by the back way while the referee sneaked out through the furnace room door, and they made their bus without being lynched, although I imagine Temple kept on chewing gum through it all.

On the way home, I didn't say anything to Tub Garrison about the star-spangled exhibition of coolness under fire. If that lesson hadn't registered, I figured it wouldn't do any good to underline it.

Not that I was sure Temple's example was going to make Tub Garrison a little iceberg in the nets. If a ham prize fighter sees the heavyweight champ doing his stuff and says, "Gosh! After this I'm gonna go in there hitting like him," it's no guarantee that he isn't going to be smacked down as per usual in his very next scrap. But I thought maybe it might make Tub a bit ashamed of himself.

After all, big-time hockey crowds didn't throw cannon crackers, or tomatoes. If a bush-leaguer like Temple could keep his goat tied up with a mob like that Harperstown gang going after him, surely a big-timer like Tub Garrison could take it in a much larger arena.

• • •

SO WE WENT into the fifth and final game. It was a sellout, of course. The pair of rail-seat tickets I mailed up to Temple "with the compliments of an admirer" could have sold for three times their face value on the street.

There was a lot of guessing in the papers as to whether I'd use Garrison or not. We carried a spare goalie, and it looked like this might be the time to give him his chance. But I thought not.

Even on big-time pro teams, the spare goalie is a problem. If your regular goalie is good, the spare goalie doesn't get enough work. And if he doesn't get work, he goes sour. If your regular goalie is no good, well, you just fire him anyhow and maybe give the spare goalie his job, and then you need another spare goalie.

I wasn't ready to gamble on our reserve backstop. I would use the kid if Garrison got hurt or blew up early in the game. But until that happened I was stringing along with the goalie who had helped us get into the Cup finals by his work over the whole season.

Garrison was grateful for that, and said so. He hadn't expected that I would play him.

"Why shouldn't I play you?" I growled at him. "I figure you've got used to that crowd by now."

The other players weren't so sure. They were a pretty quiet bunch when they took the ice. If any of them really thought the Indians had a chance to cop the Cup that night, their expressions didn't show it.

The minute Garrison came through the gate you'd have thought a thunderstorm had broken out.

"Boooooo!"

The razz smashed out and rolled down like a deafening wave. And it was all meant for him. That crowd knew Garrison was the man to beat, and that they had beaten him twice before. This time, they were really ready for him.

There was a bad note to that roar—not like the crowd at Harperstown, who hated the opposition goalie and yet respected him. This crowd jeered. They despised Garrison. It doesn't help your self-confidence much to have twelve thousand people tell you that they think you're rotten.

I took a peek down the sidelines at the rail seats I had picked out for young Temple. They were empty. They were still empty when the game got under way.

It got under way slowly and carefully. I'd told my kids to lay back and wait for the breaks—penalty breaks, especially. But the Cub coach had told his squad the same thing. It made for one- and two-man rushes, always three men back of centre ice. Cagey hockey, but not so hot for the crowd.

With nothing much to cheer for, they kept laying it on Garrison. But he seemed to be more like his usual self, keeping his eye on the puck, paying no attention to the screeching mob behind the back screen. And what they were telling him about himself was plenty.

• • •

THE CUBS GOT their first shot on goal—a long one from just inside the blue line, and although the crowd cut loose with a roar that shook the Garden, as the puck left the ice, Garrison made the stop as coolly as if it was shooting practice.

He didn't have many real tough ones to block that period, the defence being air-tight and laying back; but at least he didn't look nervous. At least it looked as if he had left his goat at home and that the crowd wasn't going to get it that night. So I began to feel better.

"He's doin' all right," I said to Sam Stegg.

"So far," grunted Sam. "Wait and see what happens if he muffs one. That's when he blows."

You could just feel the tension in the air by the time we were halfway through the second period without even the smell of a goal on either side, and the kids beginning to open up. We got a break then, when one of the Cubs drew a penalty for slashing and gave us the odd-man advantage. I sent out my first-string forwards.

"This is it!" I said. "Go get that goal."

They got it, but they had to do it the hard way. It took a ganging attack that lasted the whole two minutes and sent the crowd crazy before Hy Lennox finally beat the Cub goalie, who was lying out in the crease after making five consecutive stops.

So then we could lay back and make the Cubs carry the play.

They carried it. They were always at their best when they were trailing. All through the playoffs they had been winning their games from behind. They smashed in now like a team possessed.

Tub Garrison stood up to it. He weathered an attack that stood the defence on their heads. He kicked, batted and sprawled, took everything they had. He played goal as I knew he could play it.

"Yes, sir," I said to myself happily, "he's not letting this Temple boy top him tonight."

I took another peek down the boards. The two rail seats weren't empty any more. There sat the coach of the Stratham team with poker-faced Temple beside him, chewing gum as usual, watching the game as if it wasn't any more exciting than a chess tournament.

We went back into the dressing room still hanging onto that one-goal lead. I slapped Garrison on the back.

"You're doin' fine, boy," I told him. "Say, when you go out again take a look over at the west rail seats at the blue line. Friend Temple is watchin' you tonight."

Garrison mopped his sweating face with a towel.

"I learned something from that guy," he said.

And then, three minutes after the third frame began, the world came crashing down around me.

• • •

THE CUBS SMASHED at us right from the draw. They smashed hard and fast. They backed up our defence, they tore in with more speed than they had shown in the whole series. They flew in there like wildcats. They drove high shots and low shots at Garrison. They ganged in around the crease, and my kids couldn't break clear.

Garrison made a stop with his knee, caught the shot from the rebound on the blade of his stick and went down sprawling to bat out another with his glove. The puck skittered out beyond the crease. Bill O'Day golfed at it, but missed.

Garrison didn't have a chance when a Cub winger swooped in and lifted the puck over him into the twine.

That gave the crowd something to cheer for. And they went to work on Garrison again right from the face-off. Some yap, behind the back screen, started the old *clap-clap-clap*.

Clap-clap-clap-clap-clap-clap!

It got louder and louder, monotonous and nerve-racking. I could see Garrison looking jittery. That goal hadn't been his fault, but it left him shaken. And the crowd was finishing the job. Then I saw him look over at the rail seats near the blue line. He set his jaw and crouched in the net.

The Cubs raged in again. And this time we had trouble. Big Boy Krueger drilled a Cub into the end boards and they went down in a heap. The ref blew his whistle and thumbed Big Boy to the bench. And as if that wasn't enough, when Big Boy got up, his face was twisted and he was hanging onto his right shoulder.

You guessed it! Broken collarbone. Our ace defenceman was out.

I juggled the line-up, talking to myself while Sam Stegg went bustling off to the dressing room to look after Big Boy. I called in the forward line, sent out my two best backcheckers and a defence spare. Then they braced themselves for what was coming.

It came.

The Cubs smelled a win now. They ganged. And the *clap-clap-clap* went on and on even above the shouts and yells of that hockey-mad crowd. They stormed in close and Garrison looked shaky on the first drive that came his way. He muffed in clearing it, fell on the puck and hung on. So we had a face-off beside the net.

Tub was blowing up. I could see it. He had forgotten all about young Temple. I saw him look back up at the crowd behind the screen. It was all they needed. They jumped him in earnest then.

Clap-clap-clap!

"You're through, Garrison!"

"He's blown!"

The Cubs swarmed all around the net. Garrison floundered, missed a shot by a foot. Only the fact that it hit the post saved him. He sprawled in the crease as the puck bounced out. Amby Doran nailed it and stepped in. Comet Adams made a lunge with his stick and hooked Doran's feet from under him. Doran went down without getting the shot away.

The crowd yelled murder. And I don't blame them. Adams had lost his head. He was chased to the penalty bench and the Cubs got a penalty shot.

"This is it!" I groaned.

• • •

AS THE PLAYERS pulled off to the sidelines, my boys looked sick. The goalie blown up, ace defenceman out for the rest of the game, two men in the penalty box, the score tied and a free shot coming up!

Garrison was white. He looked back up at the crowd again. And the *clap-clap-clap* went up like thunder.

Doran raced in, crossed the blueline, took two more strides and whipped off his shot. Just as the puck left his stick, some fool in back of the screen heaved a huge fire-cracker onto the ice.

Boom!

It went off before Doran's stick hit the puck. Garrison, tense in the net, jumped. The puck sifted through the air and whipped past him into the net.

The crowd went nuts. But the referee's whistle was blowing before I could even start out onto the ice to put in a beef. The ref called back the play.

He was right, of course. But that crowd wanted to tear him limb from limb. They were boiling. About four thousand programs, nineteen hats and six dollars in coins went showering down onto the ice.

It took five minutes to clean the rubbish off the ice. And while they were clearing it to let Amby Doran try the penalty shot again, and while the ushers were giving the bum's rush to the bozo who heaved the cannon cracker, I beckoned Garrison over to me.

"Now listen, kid," I pleaded, "for the love of Pete, steady down! Forget about that crowd. Forget 'em!"

Garrison grinned at me. "Forget 'em yourself, Casey! I'm all right now."

And so help me, he was. A miracle, it seemed like. He went back in there and turned aside a shot from Doran that looked labelled from the second it left his stick. And then he settled down to give an exhibition of backstopping, with the team in front of him two men short, that goes down in my books as nothing short of hair-raising. He was like a block of ice.

The crowd worked on him until their hands and tonsils were sore. He held the fort with pads and stick and gloves until we were at strength again, all the time moving his jaws like he was chewing gum, cool and unhurried. That crowd couldn't get his goat any more. It looked like he just didn't have such an animal.

The Cubs tired themselves out firing at him. Then they got rough, and one of their wings drew a penalty for tripping. Then we had our innings when Comet Adams sifted through to combine with Hy Lennox for the slickest goal of the series. It put us back in the lead and we stayed there, although the Cubs ganged for the last five minutes and fired everything at Tub Garrison but the time clock.

They had no more punch left than a litter of kittens at the finish, and we salted away an extra goal for good measure, but it was like scoring on a team from the Huff and Puff League by that time.

• • •

WHEN THE GONG sounded and I knew I had brought a team up the long trail to the Memorial Cup at last, Tub Garrison came skating up to me, grinning all over his face.

"Kid!" I yelled. "You were wonderful! You were all wonderful! But how you stopped 'em! How you turned 'em aside! And me thinking you were ready to blow up!"

"I was, too," grunted Garrison. "They had my goat runnin' around in little circles, Casey. I forgot all about Temple, I forgot everything but that blamed *clappety-clap*. And then that bird threw the cannon cracker!"

"Why, you nearly jumped out of your pads! I figured it was your finish."

"Rats! It reminded me of that bird Temple. I said to myself, 'Golly, he never blinked an eyelash when they threw cannon crackers at him.' So I got back in there and figured I'd show him I was just as good as he was."

"Come on," I said. "We're going over and tell him. You owe him that much anyhow."

Temple and the Stratham coach were just leaving their seats when we came up.

"Temple," I said, "you don't know me, but I saw you play the other night and it was me sent you those tickets. Tub Garrison here has something to tell you."

Temple just blinked and looked puzzled. Then he reached down and fished up a little mouthpiece from under his coat. And I noticed he had a little gadget over one ear.

"You'll have to shout," said the Stratham coach. "The poor kid is deaf as a post!"

TOO SLOW TO COUNT

TIM CORDELL'S FLOW of staccato chatter was unbroken as he sparred with the Indian centre out in front of the Tiger goal cage. A short, witty, 160-pound package of dynamite dressed in Tiger blue, he dodged back and forth in front of his exasperated check, covering him so thoroughly that the other man had no chance of taking a pass that might come his way.

"Come on! Get going! Cover that wing! Watch for the pass-out!" Tim's terse yelps were keeping his wings up on their toes.

Everyone in hockey said there never was such a spark plug to throw pep into a lagging team as talkative Tim Cordell. The very sight of him in action every second he was on the ice, the incarnation of dynamic energy, was enough to stir a lagging teammate into renewed vigor, even in the dying moments of a shutout game, with the Tigers on the blank end.

He played every hockey game as if it were a Stanley Cup final, with every ounce of his 160 pounds. And here, with the score 2–0 against the Tigers and three minutes to play, he was wading in and chattering away as if the two-goal deficit didn't exist.

The Indian right-winger, scrapping for possession of the puck in the corner, suddenly scooped it clear and knocked over a wild pass.

The opposing centre made a try for it, but with Tim Cordell tying him up, he hadn't a chance. Tim knocked down his stick, darted in, scooped up the rubber and broke fast for the blue line.

"Come on!" he yipped, scooting over the line like a terrier after a tomcat. He hurdled a wildly swinging Indian stick, tore into the clear with his wings in frantic pursuit and the Indian forwards streaming madly in pursuit.

The crowd surged to its feet with a thunderous roar. Tim Cordell was away on one of his rushes again. If you hadn't seen Tim Cordell rush, you hadn't seen hockey.

He was flying as he hit the mid-ice circle, streaking toward the Indian defence, far ahead of the pack.

The mob opened its collective mouth and yelled. Whether he scored or not, it was worth the price of a box seat just to watch Tim Cordell skate.

In he went, over the blue line, down on the defence. He cut over to the right, shifted in sharply the moment the left defenceman made his move, bolted through the gap and let fly with a rising shot from in front of the net.

• • •

HOW THE GOALIE got his glove on the puck was a minor miracle. But save it he did, tipping it over the top of the goal as it glanced off and into the back screen, while the shriek of the crowd changed to a groan like a roll of thunder. And then the yell rose again, for Tim Cordell had darted around the side of the net and snagged the puck as it hit the ice.

Around the cage he swept. The goalie lunged and slid, got his skate against the post just as Tim Cordell tried to poke the puck around the corner. Tim pulled it back; out of the corner of his eye he saw a Tiger wing surging in and flicked the puck over.

The Indian goalie was good. He rose in the net like a seal and nailed the shot on his stick, deflecting the puck to the back boards.

"Pass-out!" barked Tim, and tore behind the net again, racing an Indian defenceman for the bounding rubber. If one scoring chance didn't click, Tim Cordell never high-tailed it back to centre. He simply looked for the next chance and jumped at it. Defencemen had the jitters every moment he was inside their blue line until the puck was safely cleared.

Once again, Tim Cordell got his stick on the puck. He could wriggle out of a hole with amazing dexterity; could get a pass away from any angle. Gord Gurd, the defenceman, knew it. Gurd was a beefy, bad-tempered fellow with a penalty-studded record as the league bad man.

Gurd tried to block, missed. Then, as Tim Cordell pulled out and tried to get away, Gurd hurled his big body into a smashing bodycheck.

He caught Tim with hip and shoulder, caught him and pitched him with brutal force against the boards.

Tim Cordell's light body slammed up against the barrier with a terrific impact, and he slumped to the ice in a quivering heap.

A great, rising howl of wrath surged up from the crowd. The referee's whistle blew shrilly.

Gurd, with sullen face, hooked the loose puck down the ice. One of Tim's front-line mates streaked in, hauled off and nailed Gurd with a swinging left that caught the burly defenceman by surprise, sent him reeling and stumbling to the ice.

Tim Cordell, with the breath knocked out of him and one leg twisted underneath him, made a spasmodic effort to rise, collapsed again. There was a great deal of milling and pushing around as players separated the embattled Gurd and the Tiger forward, as the referee dealt out penalties, as the Tiger trainer trotted out and knelt beside Tim.

"I'm OK, Baldy," he gasped, white-faced.

But when they helped him to his feet the left leg buckled under him. He almost pitched to the ice again. He was carried to the dressing room and the crowd settled back, murmuring.

"Torn ligament," was the doctor's verdict. "No more hockey for a long while, Tim."

• • •

IT WAS WELL past mid-season before Tim Cordell stepped out onto the ice again before a packed house of Tiger fans who leaped to their feet with a spontaneous roar of welcome.

The leg had been given the best of care; the doctors said it was as good as ever, and in the workouts Tim had been his old bustling, talkative self, full of pep, scooting around the ice like a water bug on a pond.

But Sam Bloss, coach of the Tigers, looked dubious as Tim went to centre for the face-off. It was a coincidence that the Indians were again their rivals that night.

Bert Hale, the Indian centre, shook hands with Tim and congratulated him on his return to the hockey wars.

"Thanks for the kind words," retorted Tim, "but I'm going to run you ragged tonight just the same."

For the first period the checking was hard and close, a scoreless frame, with most of the play in the neutral zone. Tim stuck to Hale like a postage stamp, outwitted him on one occasion and went in close for a hard shot on goal that sent the crowd into an uproar and the opposition goalie into a panic.

But the wings, checked off their feet at the defence, failed to back up the play, and a rebound lay uncovered, with the goalie out of his net and Tim sprawled beside the cage until an Indian wing darted in to clear it out of danger.

In the second period, Riley and Lennon, the Tiger wings, began turning on the heat, shaking off their checks and racing away at top speed.

And Tim Cordell was lagging. He couldn't keep pace with his fast-flying mates. Defensively, his backchecking had Hale tied up in knots. But on the attack his wings ran away from him.

An Indian rush was broken up at the Tiger defence, with Hale down on the ice after being flattened by a defence-man. Out came a pass from the goalie to the blue line.

Tim Cordell grabbed it, wheeled, headed down the ice. He had a clear field ahead, and Riley, over on right wing, pulled away at the same moment.

The Tiger supporters rose to their feet, cheering what looked like a scoring chance.

Tim legged it for the opposite blue line. The Indian left winger pulled up on Riley, trailing him closely, so closely that he would be able to intercept a pass if it came.

It was Tim's break, for he had a good five feet on Hale. He drew on every ounce of speed he possessed, conscious all the time that the left leg didn't have the spring it used to have.

Tim was close to the blue line now. Then Hale swept up alongside, hacking at his stick. Hale had spotted him a lead and overhauled him from blue line to blue line.

Tim rifled a desperate pass over to Riley, got it away safely just as Hale crowded him off stride. Then he saw the Indian left winger intercept the puck, whirl with it, fighting with Riley for possession.

The scoring chance was lost. The puck came zipping across to Hale. He snapped it up and streaked away. Tim

Cordell plugged doggedly in pursuit. But Hale rapidly out-distanced him, raced in for a shot from outside, crashed through for a stab at the rebound.

• • •

A TIGER DEFENCEMAN got his stick on the puck and golfed it down the ice. The whistle blew. Icing. Relief players tumbled over the boards.

Tim skated slowly over to the bench and sat down. He caught a glimpse of Riley's angry face as the winger came in. Riley was a hot-tempered, impetuous Irishman who could never curb his tongue.

"Might as well have a man in the penalty box as a centre who can't keep up with the play," snorted the fiery wing. "Half a dozen scoring chances we had, and blew them all. Look at that last play. Hale spots the puck carrier a big lead and catches him."

"Skip it, Riley!" broke in Sam Bloss curtly.

The next time the first stringers went out the story was repeated. Three times in a row Riley grabbed the puck to lead a wild Tiger rush from end to end. Three times running, with a scoring play in sight if the centre had been up with his wings to take a pass, to pull a defenceman out of position or to make a shot, Tim Cordell came lagging across the blue line with Hale covering him like a blanket.

And in the concluding stages of the last period, when it came time to send the first line out again, with the game still scoreless, Tim glanced over at Sam Bloss. But the coach's eyes passed over him, rested on Harper Winston, sub centre who had come up from the minor league for a big-time tryout.

"Go out this time, Winston!" ordered the coach.

Winston cast Tim Cordell a smug look of triumph and leaped to his feet.

There was no doubt about Winston's speed. He was a skating fool, had gone into hockey, in fact, on the strength of a brilliant amateur speed-skating record. Slim and rangy, with sharp features and black hair parted slickly in the centre, he contrasted strongly with the wiry, homely, freckle-faced Tim Cordell.

Tim crouched a little lower on the bench and watched the revamped line go to work.

The face-off was inside the Indian blue line. Hale got it, but his pass to his wing was intercepted, and the pass came to Winston. The sleek centre hurtled away with it, streaked across the line and down the rink.

Hale burned up the ice trying to overtake Winston. But the speed artist increased his lead. Riley and Lennon were up with him, skating like mad; but at that, Winston beat them across the blue line.

The defence spread out to meet the attack. Gurd braced himself for a bodycheck, but Winston whipped the puck over to Riley, just coming in, and swung over. Gurd got back in time to bump Riley while his mate rode Lennon out of the play.

Riley went down with a smash, but he hadn't tried for the net.

In the split second he had for his shot he drifted the puck over to Winston, uncovered at the side of the net. It clicked against Winston's stick. He whipped it inside the near post just as the goalie slid across the cage.

The Tiger supporters howled their glee. The scoreless tie was broken with only a few minutes to play.

Tim Cordell's face was expressionless.

• • •

COACH SAM BLOSS gave him every chance, but in the next two weeks it became evident that Tim was through so far as the first line of forwards was concerned. The leg hadn't come back. Tim Cordell had lost the blinding speed that had been his greatest asset. Riley and Lennon were ineffective when they had to slow down to his pace.

Similarly on the second line, Tim didn't click. He couldn't hold his own with the fast-skating youngsters on the wings.

More and more, Bloss began using him on the relief trio, the backchecking third stringers sent out there to hold the fort when the team was short-handed through a penalty, or when the Tigers were stalling to protect a slim lead.

Tim was as game as they come, afraid of no man on skates, and he still pitched into every match as if it were a playoff; but goals weren't expected of the third line, and the cheers of the mob go to the goal getters.

Tim Cordell lost his hold on the fans. He was just a scrappy, hard-working utility man now. There was a veteran named Holliday on the sub list who was one of the best defensive centres in the game, and Holliday was used on the third line quite as often as Tim.

The bench warming would have been easier to take had it not been for the patronizing attitude of Harper Winston.

"Too bad you're not about twenty pounds heavier," Winston said to Tim one evening after a game in which Tim had seen only three minutes of action. "They'd be able to make a defenceman out of you. Too bad to see a player of your age warmin' the bench all the time. Speed doesn't count on defence, but you've sure gotta have it if you want to get anywhere as a forward."

The tactless speech burned Tim up. Through, was he?

• • •

SAM BLOSS BEGAN to notice that when the Tigers were at home, Tim Cordell and Stuffy Holmes, the goalie, were always in uniform and on the ice by the time the other players arrived for the morning workout.

He asked Holmes about it. The goalie, a big-hearted youngster who had worshipped Tim Cordell when the flying centre was at his best, looked embarrassed.

"Aw, we just check in a little ahead of time so Tim can give me a little extra practice," he said.

"You mean so Tim can get some extra practice," retorted Bloss shrewdly. "What's the idea?"

"He's just trying to brush up on his shooting, Sam, that's all. I feel kinda sorry for him. All washed up and still taking extra shooting practice."

But the shooting practice didn't make much difference. More and more Holliday got the call when it came time to send out the third line. They used Tim sometimes in games that were irretrievably lost.

One day he came to Bloss and said: "I guess there won't be a problem if I take a leave of absence, Sam? Without pay, of course."

"Why, I guess not, Tim. What's up?"

"I found a fellow who says he might be able to do something for this leg of mine. Electric treatments of some kind. But I'll have to stop playing hockey for the rest of the season. If I strain the leg it will ruin everything."

Sam Bloss shook Tim's hand. "Good luck to you, kid. Take all the time you want. And I hope when you come back next season you'll show your heels to the whole pack of 'em the way you used to."

• • •

THE TIGERS FOUGHT their way through a hard season to win their division championship, and early spring found them stacked up against their old enemies, the Indians, in the three-out-of-five series.

They didn't get there without a struggle. They just limped in under the wire after a mauling two-game battle with the Bears; a battle that put Holliday out of the big series with a broken rib and left every member of the squad bumped and bruised.

Bloss sent down to their minor-league team for reserves, and three eager youngsters were sent up to have their chance as relief players. But the Tigers lost their opening game by a 3–1 score against a team that was in better shape, dropped the second by a 2–1 margin and were regarded as out of the hunt.

When the squad entrained for the out-of-town games, gloomily aware of the fact that the Indians needed only one more victory to take the Cup, Tim Cordell was with them.

"I'm going to see those games if I have to pay my own way," he told Sam Bloss. "After all, I'm still a member of the team."

"Sure you are," answered Bloss. "You come along, Tim. Gosh, how we could use you now if only that leg of yours . . ."

"The treatments are helping a lot, but I've got to be careful. I'll be showing you some speed again next season."

It was a desperate team that pitched in against the Indians in the third game. And all through that hectic struggle the staccato voice of Tim Cordell urged the players on from the sidelines.

"Step into him! Chase him, Lennon! Grab that pass! Watch that man, Riley! Tear into 'em, boys!"

And in the dressing room, between periods, with the Tigers trailing by a goal, Tim Cordell was there throwing confidence into them, insisting that they had the Indians on the run.

"You've got 'em licked! Licked, I tell you. They're ready to crack. Keep at them."

Whether it was the inspiration of Tim's urgent chatter or sheer desperation on the part of a squad that saw hockey's most coveted prize slipping out of its grasp, the Tigers ripped into their rivals in the last period of that game so fiercely that the Indians, every bit as leg-weary, cracked.

Three goals the Tigers counted in that wild frame, three goals that pulled them back into the running once more. And in the next game they smashed into the Indians again, with Tim Cordell begging, imploring, cheering, talking himself into a lather of perspiration, and squeezed out a bitterly fought 3–2 win to put themselves back on even terms, with the rubber game on home ice.

But it was costly. Of the whole team, Winston and a couple of the new relief men were the only players who came out of that torrid struggle unmarked. The Indians were a bruising, hard-checking crew.

Baldy, the trainer, shook his head dispiritedly as he bustled around attending to bumps, bruises, sprains, charley horses, cuts and black eyes.

"The team is shot," the old trainer confided to Tim Cordell. "I've been conditioning hockey players for years, Tim, and this team is in no shape to win the next game. I'm tellin' you, the Indians will win on condition."

Tim went to Sam Bloss. "Put me on the line-up for that game, will you, Sam?"

The coach gaped at him. "You're crazy, Tim. I wouldn't dare do it. For your own sake. The doctor said you'd be all right again if you stayed out of hockey until next season."

"Doctor be hanged! Send me in there tonight if you need me!"

• • •

SO TIM CORDELL dressed for the final game against the Indians, the game upon which a championship depended. They will talk about that game long after all the Tigers and Indians who took part in it have hung up their sticks forever.

It began tamely enough, with the battered Tigers following their coach's instructions to cover their checks, to stay back, to let the Indians carry the play to them, to wait for a break.

For the whole first period and for ten minutes of the second period it went like that—close and hard. The Indians, banking on superior condition to win, were taking no chances.

Midway in the second period a Tiger defenceman drew a penalty for tripping. It was the break the Indians had been waiting for. They cut loose with a gang attack that smashed through the reeling Tiger line, that sent the puck skittering in the Tiger defence area as they rained shots on the goal, swooped in for rebounds, checked every desperate Tiger attempt to clear.

Over on the players' bench, Tim Cordell was shouting: "Fight 'em! Step into 'em! Clear it! Clear it!"

The Tigers fought back like a super team. But it ended with Stuffy Holmes sprawled outside the cage, the puck in the back of it, a defenceman lying on the ice near the boards and the Indian centre on his knees just as he had been when he let go the drive from a double pass at one side of the goal.

It looked mountainous, that lone counter in the second period, and it loomed bigger and bigger as the game went on into the third with the Indians back in their shell, laying down a wall of sticks at their own blue line, defying the tired, stumbling Tigers to break through.

Tim Cordell was yelling like a maniac. "Go in! Go in on them! Take a chance! Pitch into 'em!"

And at intervals he was pleading with Sam Bloss. "Let me go out there, Sam. Just once."

And the coach said quietly, "Not yet, Tim."

Sam Bloss had seen a great deal of hockey in his time. He was thinking of Tim Cordell's leg—the leg that might put Tim back into the gallery of hockey's great if it got the rest it needed, if it didn't incur a strain.

Then came the break Sam Bloss knew would come.

Winston had the puck, going up at centre on another of those rushes that had broken so many times against the Indian defence. Up he went, still sleek and unmarked, because somehow Winston never had the puck when a bodycheck was coming; somehow he always seemed to have the speed to flash out of those jams that had trapped other forwards. Hale was skating backward, watching him, stick poised, ready to strike.

And then—it may have been a small crack in the scarred ice that did it—Hale stumbled. He didn't lose his balance, he didn't fall. But for a moment he was thrown out of that smooth rhythm; he faltered. And Winston spurted, went around him, darted in, flashing the puck across to Riley just as he hit the defence.

Riley snagged the puck and shot in one motion. Screened by a defenceman, the flying rubber shot low toward the net, struck one of the goalie's pads, deflected, struck the post and glanced inside.

The roar that went up then was like the roar of an earthquake. The score was tied! The stumbling Tigers were still in the hunt!

• • •

AND TIED IT REMAINED until the gong clattered its brassy signal to end the period. Suspense hung over the packed rink like a cloud. The telegraph instruments and the typewriters clicked and chattered.

Then began the struggle that was to make this game one of the most memorable in the history of hockey.

Into the first overtime period they went, cautious, desperate, each team knowing that one false move might give the other team a break and the winning goal.

A rush, a long shot, perhaps a hacking scrimmage around the net with the crowd frantic, and then back they would come, waiting for the counterattack.

It went on like that, on through the first period of overtime, on through the second. And the gong rattled out again with the teams deadlocked.

The players were horribly tired now. The last game of a long, hard season, the last game that had to be played to a finish. If it took all night, that game would have to be played through until one team or the other made the light blink to signal the winning of a championship.

The forwards would come crawling out of the box, would skate and weave their way through three minutes that seemed like three hours, and back they would come, scarcely able to lift one steel-shod foot after the other.

They would sag on the bench like dead men, while the substitutes took up that apparently endless struggle out there under the glaring lights on the choppy surface, bitten and scored and streaked by the steel blades.

• • •

SIXTY MINUTES of overtime they played, an entire extra game, and the deadlock was unbroken. There had been dozens of close calls as each team stirred itself to frantic spasmodic flurries that brought them inside the defensive zones. But the goalies, fresher than any of the padded figures out there, turned all the shots aside.

It was getting easier for the goalies now. The teams were dead on their feet. There was no zip, no punch to the occasional shots that came toward the nets.

Tim Cordell grabbed his coach by the sleeve and pleaded with him: "Sam, you need me out there. You need me. I've been costing you an extra man all night. Why did you let me dress for the game if you meant me to warm a bench? Those boys are dying on their feet. I'm fresh, ready to go."

"Tim. It was your doctor. I promised him. He said if you strained that leg it would finish your chance of ever making a comeback. It's for your own sake, boy."

"Comeback, nothing! Let me go out there, Sam. Just for three minutes."

Sam Bloss was tempted. One fresh man, even a crippled crock like Tim Cordell, might swing the scales. He hesitated. And then he shook his head.

"Nothing doing, Tim. I think we can win without ruining you for next season."

Tim slumped back on the bench, muttering.

On into the seventy-fourth minute of overtime. Harper Winston had the puck at his own blue line, going up slowly, feet dragging, body crouched over like a man about to fall.

Riley, with a great strip of plaster blocking the vision of one eye, with his ribs under the jersey taped to protect a blue welter of bruises, plugged wearily along the wing.

Lennon, with plaster on jaw and forehead, his right ankle so badly swollen that he had to keep his teeth clenched to keep from crying out with the pain, dragged himself along the other boards.

Winston passed mid-ice. Hale's stick shot out, but Winston flipped the puck between Hale's feet, plunged around him, picked up the disc again.

The tired, hoarse crowd surged forward. Winston teetered up to the blue line with Hale stumbling behind. He passed the puck to Riley, but Riley was hard checked, got it, flung it back.

Gurd, the defenceman, smashed into Winston. A fair bodycheck, with all the last reserve of Gurd's flagging strength. And Winston went down. He went down like an empty wheat sack flung to a floor, and he lay there with his head buried in his arms, on top of the puck.

He wasn't hurt. But when the referee stopped the play

and they hauled him to his feet, Winston was babbling as he shouldered them aside and lurched toward the box.

"I won't stay in here! I won't stay! Take me out. It's too much. I can't stay any longer." Winston had cracked.

The shoulders of Sam Bloss drooped. This was the finish. His eyes fell along the line of haggard, sagging faces. The second stringers had just come in, exhausted. His third-line centre was just a youngster from the minor league, a kid who had been thumped and battered so unmercifully that he could scarcely stand on his feet now.

"Chief," gritted Tim Cordell's voice, "whether you like it or not, I'm going out there."

And Tim Cordell clambered over the fence, dropped to the ice.

Sam Bloss reached out, tried to stop him. "Tim!" he shouted. "Come back here. I won't let you. I promised your doctor . . ."

"Who cares?" yelled Tim Cordell, and swung up to centre. "Come on, kid!" he barked at Riley. "They're just as tired as you are. We'll get 'em." And to Lennon. "Snap into it, Lenny! I'm gonna hand you some passes, boy."

● ● ●

FROM THE FACEOFF, when he struck hard and savagely and stole the puck from the weary Hale, he made good on that promise. A swift pass to Lennon and the Tigers were on the attack again. A pass back and Tim Cordell had it. He didn't rush. He fired from just inside the Indian blue line, and it was the most vicious shot the mob had seen since the start of the overtime, certainly the most vicious long shot any of the Tigers had ever seen Tim uncork.

Right through the defence it blazed, streaking for the lower corner. The goalie pounced on it in the nick of time, stopped it, cleared it to the corner. Tim Cordell was barking at his wings: "Keep after 'em! Keep 'em in there!"

He was slow, very slow, because he dared not take any chances with that leg, and the stumbling wings were no faster. They could not get in quickly enough to hold the play in the Indian defensive zone.

Hale took a pass and broke away. He broke past Tim, and Sam Bloss groaned when he saw that even Hale, exhausted as he was by the long grind, out-footed Tim over the blue line.

Hale went down, but they stopped him at the defence, and although the wing who went down with him got a try at the net, the Tigers hurled back the attack.

There seemed to be a little extra punch in the way they flung back the raiders, what with Tim Cordell yelping, "Stop 'em! Lay into 'em! We've got 'em on the run now," and when he got the puck again he slogged slowly up the middle lane again, holding the puck in spite of all Hale's desperate efforts to throw him off stride, and when he reached the defence he let drive another of those long shots.

Long shots hold few terrors for goalkeepers, for the man in the net has time to judge them. But this long shot, considering the distance, had the speed of a bullet, and the goalie had to do the splits to make the save. But he made it, and again the Indians struck back.

They smashed back, with Tim Cordell hurling himself savagely into the fight, checking Hale to a standstill; back into the Tiger defensive zone, with Tim chattering, yipping away at his mates, throwing a last spark of vitality into the reeling crew.

Two minutes went by, and Sam Bloss called in the line and sent out his second stringers. What was needed was a forward who could work in close on that goal, and Tim Cordell wasn't fast enough to do that. And then the crowd roared when Tim waved back the relief centre, stayed in there over Sam's protests.

The fight went on. Every once in a while Tim got his stick on that puck close enough to let drive another of those blistering long shots. They came close, but not close enough. And when the Indians came back on the attack he was in the thick of it, trading bump for bump, intercepting passes, clearing the puck out of danger, throwing new spirit into the squad.

• • •

THE INDIANS WERE floundering all over the ice by now. The overtime period was becoming a nightmare. Even the crowd could scarcely raise a cheer any more. And when the teams changed ends, Sam Bloss sent Riley and Lennon out there again.

"Chief," said Riley, "I've got one dying kick left in me, but if it hadn't been for that little gamecock out there I wouldn't know I had it. Let me take one more bang at 'em."

And out they came, Riley and Lennon, crippled and leaden-footed. Where they got it from no one knew; but from the face-off when Tim snared the puck and snapped it across to Lennon, they showed speed—one last burst of speed. Down they went, outsmarting their checks.

They surged over the line. Riley let fly a high shot that just cleared the net and bounced off the back screen. Lennon went in. Gurd, the defenceman, loomed in Tim's path, shoulder hunched.

Tim piled into him, and Gurd, exhausted, gave way, crumpled up like a rag doll, sprawled to the ice, just as Lennon took a despairing swipe at the puck and sent it spinning out in front.

Tim lunged at it. His shoulders tensed. He fired. Not a long shot this time, but a drive from ten feet out, and it smoked into the upper corner of that net while the goalie was still halfway across the cage.

It whacked into the netting, tumbled to the ice, and the red light blinked as the crowd surged to its feet with a great long-drawn roar of released tension.

The Tigers had won. Outlucked, outconditioned, but not outgamed, the Tigers had won.

"But where did you develop the shot?" demanded Sam Bloss later. "You used to get by on playmaking. You step in there tonight with a shot like you've never had before."

Tim Cordell grinned. "I've been practicing," he said. "I figured if I wasn't ever going to be fast enough to get up there with the wings again, I'd better be able to get the puck up there, anyway.

"Just wait until next winter, Sam. The doc was wild because I played tonight, but he says I didn't harm the leg, after all. Next season, with my speed back and a shot I never had before—watch my smoke, Sam!"

"I've seen it," grunted Sam Bloss.

THEY DIDN'T KNOW HOCKEY

DAN HAWLEY SNAGGED the goalie's pass-out just inside the blue line and whirled away with the puck. Judge, the opposing centre, swooped in and tried to check him, but Dan hurdled Judge's stick, shot the rubber ahead and snapped it up again a moment later as he raced down the middle lane with Judge hard at his heels.

There was less than a minute to play and the score was tied with the teams nearing the limit of their overtime. The visiting Owls would be well satisfied with a tie, but Dan Hawley knew as well as anyone in the rink that anything but a win on home ice would be almost fatal to the Panthers' chances of grabbing the league title.

He streaked toward the Owl goal with the crowd whooping in a frenzy. There was an imploring, hysterical note in the roar of the mob. The Panther fans were begging for that goal; the one goal that would squeeze out a win; the goal that seemed impossible to get and that must be scored within the next fifty seconds, if it was to be scored at all.

Dan was tired, for it had been a long, grim game, and bush-league amateurs are expected to go the distance. He could hear the click and chop of Judge's skates as the Owl centre tried to overhaul him, but Dan knew he could out-foot Judge. He wasn't worrying about that.

But this next scoring play. It had to click. It had to be perfect. There mustn't be a slip-up. If it missed, there wouldn't be time for another. And both of his wings were covered.

The Owls had a hard-hitting defence. And their goalie was smart. Dan streaked in and fired from outside.

It was a hard, low, wicked shot, but the high-pitched roar of the crowd changed to a long, deep groan. You couldn't beat the Owl goalie on long shots. Everyone knew that. And this shot, moreover, was wide of the net.

The puck spanked against the rear boards with a thud that could be heard the length of the rink.

The left defenceman swung around. And the Owl left winger, covering his check along the boards, began hot-footing it into the corner to pick up the rebound.

But Dan Hawley was already sifting through for that same rebound. He had shot purposely wide; he knew the exact angle at which the puck would ricochet from the boards; he knew exactly where he could pick it up.

It was perfectly timed. He was in like a streak. He got his stick on the puck as it skimmed across the ice on its rebound from the boards. And in the same motion, he pivoted and laid down a swift pass to his uncovered right winger, Ben Borstall.

• • •

THE PLAY HAD pulled all the Owls out of position. Borstall swooped in, went right to the net, saw that Steve O'Hara, the left winger, was uncovered and backing him up. Borstall faked a shot that pulled the goalie over, then banged the puck over to O'Hara.

And O'Hara socked the rubber into the upper corner for a perfect goal.

The crowd went wild. They went stark raving mad with joy, seemed ready to tear down the rink in their enthusiasm. They were still in a frenzy of rejoicing when the game ended a few moments later. A mob of fans carried O'Hara off the ice. And scores of them crowded around Ben Borstall, pounding him on the back.

"Ben deserves credit too, don't forget!" bellowed one of the fans. "O'Hara scored that goal all right, but Ben gave him the pass."

A lot of people had nice things to say to Dan Hawley, too. "Nice game, Dan." "You were sure flyin' out there tonight, Dan." But for that matter every member of the team came in for his share of hero worship.

O'Hara, however, occupied the limelight. Wasn't he the league's leading scorer? And hadn't he banged home the winning goal?

"We won't be able to keep him here very long," said someone. "Some of the pro teams will be after him before we know it. A goal-getter like O'Hara would make good anywhere."

Dan Hawley, getting out of his uniform in the dressing room, grinned cynically. After all, what did the average fan know about hockey strategy? So far as Dan was concerned, he didn't care who got the credit, as long as the Panthers won the game.

It was only a small amateur league consisting of teams from half a dozen towns in the North country, but the winter series generated enough heat and excitement to set a big-time pro circuit on fire. Every man, woman and child in Harrisville, hometown of the Panthers, talked hockey from

December to March. If there were any more rabid followers of the game, they lived in Pennifer, hometown of the Owls.

• • •

BUT IF DAN WAS philosophical about his lack of recognition as the mainstay of the Panther team, Mary King was not. Mary was Dan's girl; and when he met her, as was his custom, after the game to escort her home, he was astonished to find her in bad humour.

"How long are you going to stand for this, Dan?" she demanded.

"Stand for what?" he asked in surprise.

"Letting Steve O'Hara and Ben Borstall steal all the glory," she snapped. "This town would give Steve O'Hara the Town Hall tonight, if he asked for it. The league's leading goal-getter! Good old Steve! He pulled the game out of the fire. He gave us the goal we needed. He's the white-haired boy. It makes me sick."

"Well, honey, of course the crowd can only see the guy who scores the goal."

"Why don't *you* score 'em? Steve O'Hara and Ben Borstall wouldn't get a goal all winter if you weren't there to give them the passes!"

"I dunno," objected Dan. "Maybe I could have beat that goalie, but I figured I'd better make a play of it, see. I knew if I shot wide of the net, it would pull 'em out of position and open things up a little. And it worked out just like I thought it would."

"And Steve O'Hara and Ben get all the credit. I'll bet more than half the people in that rink tonight thought you tried to score and couldn't even hit the net."

"Aw, who cares? We won, didn't we?"

"Well, I'm pretty sick of seeing Steve and Ben walking off with all the high-scoring records! Why, do you know what I heard tonight? A man in that crowd actually said: 'Isn't it too bad Hawley isn't a goal-scorer like O'Hara and Borstall? If he was, we'd have a forward line that would beat any team in the country.'"

Dan grinned. "That guy didn't know hockey."

"Show them that you *are* a goal-scorer," urged Mary. "You go out there like a big, good-natured goof and let the other fellows get all the goals, and you don't get any thanks for it."

"As long as the team wins ..."

"Won't the team win just the same if *you* score the goals? You've got to get a little gumption, Dan. Those fellows are getting all the praise and you're doing all the work. First thing you know, they'll be getting offers from the big professional teams and you'll be left behind because ..."

"Do you know, Mary, I think I'm good enough to catch a place with a pro team—"

"Of course you are. But how will you ever get there? You won't go down to the city for a tryout. Sometimes you make me tired. Working in a small-town tannery for eighteen dollars a week when you could be making hundreds of dollars for playing hockey."

"Now, Mary, you know how it is. I couldn't afford to take the time off work to go down for a tryout. Anyhow, if I'm good enough, it won't take long for the pro scouts to look me up and make me an offer."

"They're more liable to come looking for the league's leading goal-getter instead, after you've built up his record for him," sniffed Mary.

• • •

IT WAS TRUE ENOUGH, as Mary said, that Dan lacked assertiveness. Mary's desire to stir him up a little may have been due to her objection to marrying a man who didn't earn any more than eighteen dollars a week, and to her conviction that Dan could be making a great deal more if he capitalized on his hockey ability.

Dan shrugged off her remarks. After all, most girls didn't understand very much about hockey.

Next day, however, when the weekly issue of the Harrisville *Banner* appeared, and Dan read the account of the Panthers' victory over the Owls, he frowned and crumpled up the sheet in disgust.

The story read:

With less than a minute to go, Steve O'Hara, goal-getting left winger of the Harrisville Panthers, banged home the winning tally that gave the locals a win over the Pennifer Owls in a hard-fought County League fixture on local ice last night.

O'Hara's brilliant counter proved conclusively that his standing at the head of the league scorers is no accident. He outsmarted the Owl goalie and drove home a high corner shot from a difficult angle after taking a smart pass from Ben Borstall at the goal mouth.

The winning goal came in the dying stages of the final overtime period, just after Dan Hawley had plunged Panther fans into despair by missing the net on a shot from outside the defence.

Dan was mad to the toes. "Missed the net!" he exploded. "So that's what they think. By gosh, Mary was right. I make a scoring play for the winning goal. Of all the ignorance!"

At hockey practice next evening, Dan waited to hear some of the Panthers pass a remark about the *Banner's* misstatement; but although everyone had read the account, apparently no one saw anything out of the way in the newspaper's version of the scoring play. Dan went through the workout with a scowl on his lean face.

And Mary rubbed it in. "What did I tell you?" she said later that evening. "Instead of giving you credit, they think you just made a poor shot."

"I'll show 'em if I'm a poor shot," Dan said warmly.

Their next game against the Owls was at Pennifer.

• • •

SPORTS FOLLOWERS who think that a packed house at Madison Square Garden, or the Montreal Forum, represents the ultimate in hockey fever have never seen a real, bang-up, small-town, amateur clash between teams that have been bitter rivals from way back when.

A special train carried a roaring mob of Panther fans to the game. The rush seat line-up extended half a block down

Pennifer's main street two hours before the box office opened. Arguments raged hotly on every street corner.

The league race was so close that a victory away from home meant everything. Both the Owls and the Panthers were practically invincible on their own ice. A loss, or a tie, on the home pond would leave them trailing. And this night, the Panthers were out to perform the miracle.

It was a smashing struggle right from the gong. Dan Hawley, patrolling his centre lane, knew that this was the sort of game that would be decided by the breaks.

The referee, imported from a city one hundred miles away, had handled many a wild donnybrook in his time and knew all about the terrific rivalry engendered by these intertown clashes.

In the first five minutes, he served notice that he intended to keep this battle under control; he handed out two quick penalties to each team for minor offences that might have gone with a warning under other circumstances.

Dan led half a dozen rushes into Owl territory, but the defence held firm and the backchecking was close. The counterattacks were hard, smashing efforts. He had to plug hard to keep Judge tied up. Play swept from end to end at a hurricane gait to the accompaniment of a great incessant roar from every corner of the packed arena.

Dan was cagey. There would be a break sooner or later. He had a feeling that the team scoring the first goal would win this game. And midway in the period, the break occurred; a break for the Panthers.

Dan had led a rush that was broken up at the Owl blue line, with the puck in the corner and Ben Borstall tearing in after it.

Gunby, an Owl defenceman, reached it first, tried to clear and fumbled the disc. Borstall pounced on it. Gunby, realizing the danger of a pass-out, smashed into Borstall and slammed him hard against the boards with stick and knee.

The whistle shrilled. The referee thumbed Gunby to the penalty bench.

The partisan crowd let out a howl of indignation. The Owls, short-handed, lined up for the face-off in their own zone.

Dan struck swiftly when the puck fell, stabbed the rubber and banged it back to Borstall; but the Owl winger intercepted and golfed the puck down the ice. The Panthers had to go back for it. They wheeled at mid-ice and returned in formation, racing in.

Dan had the puck. He streaked across the blue line after outwitting Judge, glanced over and saw that O'Hara was in the clear and waiting for a pass. Dan tore in, shifted around the defenceman and had a clear road to the net.

O'Hara cut in sharply. It was a perfect set-up for a passing play. Dan gave no pass. From ten feet out, he simply whipped a low shot that blazed between the goalie's feet into the twine.

"That," said Dan to himself, "will show 'em if I can beat a goalie."

• • •

THAT WAS THE only goal scored in the first period. The Panthers had the edge now, for the Owls had to come to them in desperate efforts to tie up the game. In the dressing room at the end of the frame, there was an electric atmosphere of confidence.

"Nice goal, Dan," said Toby Mackenzie, the Panther coach, as he slapped Dan's back. "That's the way to cross him up. He was playing O'Hara for the shot. You had a soft one."

Dan bristled. A soft one, eh?

"Nothing soft about it," he grunted. "If you think I only had to push that puck across the line to score, you're crazy. It was going a mile a minute, and right where I wanted it. That shot would have beaten any big-league goalie."

Mackenzie gaped at Dan. "Oh, it was a good shot, Dan. I didn't mean that. A swell shot—but I mean, you crossed up the goalie ..."

He stammered, confused.

"I beat the goalie with a straight shot, that's all the crossing up I did," snapped Dan. "Trouble is, I've been feeding pucks to O'Hara and Borstall, and building up scoring credits for 'em so long that none of you fellows will believe your eyes when I show you I pack a shot, too."

Mackenzie gulped. This sort of talk from mild-mannered Dan Hawley knocked him right off his feet.

"Paddy Garner is out there tonight, Dan," he said, in an altered voice.

Paddy Garner was a scout for the major-league Redmen.

"So what?" growled Dan.

Mackenzie blinked and moved away. Apparently his usually good-natured centre was in a bad mood. Wonder what riled him, the coach reflected.

For all his apparent indifference to the mention of Paddy Garner, Dan was keenly interested in knowing that the Redmen's scout was on hand. A big-league berth was Dan's objective, and Paddy Garner's stamp of approval had sent plenty of smart amateurs up to the loop where the big money was dispersed.

When Dan skated out for the second period, it was with a determination to show Paddy Garner an eighteen-carat goal-getting forward in action.

He did it, too. Dan had plenty on the ball. He was a fast skater, a brilliant stickhandler and a hard backchecker. More than that, he had the natural hockey instinct that makes the difference between the first rater and the run-of-the-mill puck chaser.

A big-time scout didn't often get up into this league during the season. Paddy Garner saw a centre gone wild.

• • •

DAN HAWLEY GAVE everything he had. He was boring in constantly, breaking up Owl rushes before they got under way, hurling himself in on the attack, barking savagely at his wings.

He blazed shots constantly at the Owl goalie, wicked, whistling shots that kept the netminder on the jump. And midway in the period, he engineered a shifty play that pulled the defence apart, brought him right in on the goal with Ben Borstall carrying the puck.

Ben faked a shot. The goalie lunged for it, came out sprawling. It was an open net. Borstall had the cage at his mercy.

"Pass it!" snarled Dan.

Automatically, Ben slapped the puck across to him just as the goalie swung frantically with his stick. Dan swerved around the prostrate figure and flipped the rubber into the net.

To the crowd it looked as if Borstall had simply played safe. The Panther fans went wild with delight. The Owls got that goal back again a few minutes later when the substitutes were out and a Panther wing drew a penalty for tripping, but that was the only counter they got all evening.

In the final frame, the Panther first stringers went raging in on the attack again with Dan Hawley as the spearhead. He forced his wings to feed him the puck for try after try; in the end, he was rewarded by his third goal of the evening when he broke through, flanked by his wings, faked a pass to O'Hara and beat the goalie cleanly.

It was a big night for the Panthers and a big night for Dan Hawley. For the moment, he was the hero of Harrisville.

The *Banner* began its hysterical account of the game:

Sharp-shooting Dan Hawley, eagle-eyed centre of the Panthers, scored all three goals to make a single-handed job of taking the Pennifer Owls to camp last night in the most thrilling game of the season.

And Mary, delighted, said: "There! See what you can do when you try to score goals for yourself. I'll bet that will make them sit up and take notice. Steve O'Hara never scored all the goals in one game."

• • •

IT LOOKED AS IF the Panthers had the series clinched. They would have the advantage of home ice in their next game with the Owls, and it was a long time since the Panthers had been beaten at home.

Dan Hawley was a little disappointed that he didn't hear from Paddy Garner after his three-goal scoring spree in Pennifer. Nothing had happened.

If Garner had been impressed, the word didn't get back to the Panther dressing room. But Mary was confident that Dan would hear from the Redmen in a big way before next season rolled around.

The Panthers had three other games, against the third-
and fourth-place outfits, before their decisive clash with
the Owls. They won the first two—a loss in either case
would have been an upset comparable to the fall of
Jericho—and Dan Hawley checked in a total of five goals.

But Toby Mackenzie was worried. "That forward line
ain't clicking," he said to Si Clarke, the trainer.

"You're tellin' me," replied Si. "It used to be a machine.
Now it's just three hockey players."

"I guess I can't kick," Toby muttered. "They're winning
games. They're getting goals. But just the same . . ."

"Just the same, that forward line ain't what it used to
be," Si declared. "Used to be that Dan Hawley was the best
playmaker I've laid eyes on in amatoor hockey. He'd make
the plays, open up the defence, lay down the passes, and
the other two lads would bang 'em in. Now he wants to
make the plays and bang in the goals, too. The boys ain't
working together any more."

It came to a head in a game against the Kingfish, the
third-ranked team in the league.

The Kingfish were a hard-luck crew. Although they had-
n't taken a game all season, no one could ever take them for
granted. Hockey is an uncertain game, and the Kingfish out-

fit was an uncertain team. If on their home ice they per-
formed the miracle of knocking off the Panthers, it would
tie up the Panthers and the Owls for first place in games
won and lost.

"Don't take any chances against these birds!" warned
Toby Mackenzie before his team took the ice. "We don't
want any upsets at this stage of the race."

And for the first period, the game followed the usual
course of any Panther-Kingfish fixture. The humble
Kingfish couldn't get their attack clicking, their defence was
wide open, and their goalie fanned on two soft long shots.

These goals were checked in by the Panther sub forward line; but the O'Hara-Hawley-Borstall combination
scored a couple more, Dan Hawley banging in each goal
on passes from his wings. And the Kingfish didn't even
come close to crashing the scoring column.

But in the second period, evidently working on the
theory that the game was already in the bag, Steve O'Hara
and Borstall decided it would be a good chance to fatten
up their scoring averages.

Dan led a rush right up to the Kingfish defence, slipped
a pass over to O'Hara, then broke through and banged the
ice sharply for the return pass.

It didn't come. O'Hara cut in sharply from the side and let drive. The puck whizzed for the corner and deflected off the goalie's stick into the net.

Dan looked over at his wing and glared. He had called for a pass and hadn't gotten it.

• • •

A FEW MINUTES LATER, with Borstall carrying the puck down the boards on an end-to-end rush, Dan struggled clear of a defenceman and fought his way to the front of the goal for a pass from the corner.

Borstall didn't give it to him. Instead, Borstall swooped around the back of the cage and tried to bat the puck in from the side. The goalie got his skate on it in the nick of time.

"What's the big idea?" Dan growled at Borstall. "I was waiting for that pass right on the doorstep."

"You'll wait," snapped Borstall. "There's more than you can get goals on this team."

From then on, the Panther forward line failed to click. O'Hara and Borstall made strictly solo plays around the net. Combination was forgotten. Passing went by the boards.

Dan got sore. They weren't going to pass to him, huh? Well, he'd show them.

It was every man for himself, then. And the Kingfish, greatly to their own surprise, sifted through a forward line that had forgotten to backcheck and went in for an easy goal.

The Kingfish attack braced up. They smashed in again. A Panther defenceman drew a penalty. The Kingfish ganged in, socked home another counter. Their home-town crowd, sensing that the Panther attack had lost its punch, and that the Kingfish were on the upgrade, shrieked encouragement. The Kingfish played as if inspired and hacked their way through for a third goal.

The Panthers were snarling at one another in the dressing room when the period came to an end.

"If we had any backchecking up front they wouldn't be coming in like that," shouted the defencemen. "Can't expect us to do *all* the work."

"If I got a pass once in a while, I'd maybe get a goal or two," grunted O'Hara.

"That goes for me, too," snarled Borstall.

Dan yelled: "How about that time I was waiting right in front of the net for a pass-out, and you tried to score on your lonesome? A fine mess you made of it, with a sure goal waiting for us!"

"Why should I pass to you, you puck hog!" Borstall shouted. "If you ever passed back it would be different."

"I've given you a pass for every goal you've scored this winter, you punk!"

Borstall scrambled over a bench and squared off at Dan. "Don't call me a punk!"

"And don't call me a puck hog!"

Toby Mackenzie, panting with anxiety, waded between them. "Lay off! Lay off, for Pete's sake!" he pleaded. "You boys got a game to win tonight. If the Kingfish take us, we're tied with the Owls. Get together, fellows, and play hockey."

But all Toby's efforts to settle the row went for nothing. The third period was wild. Dan Hawley raced through time and again, trying to score single-handed. He didn't get one pass from his wings. Nor did O'Hara and Borstall get a pass from him. The Panthers went to pieces.

The Kingfish, playing way over their heads, knocked off two more goals to tie up the game and then went in to grab the win on a ganging attack with a minute left to play.

• • •

IT WAS A CRESTFALLEN crew of Panthers that returned to Harrisville. A defeat by the Owls now would mean the loss of the championship.

"Now maybe they'll wake up and realize what you mean to the team!" said Mary when Dan Hawley told her about the game. "When O'Hara and Borstall start trying to score goals by themselves, they can't do it. They'll be giving passes to you in the next game. You wait and see."

The next game was the high spot of the season. The league championship hung on the outcome, and although no one outside the county ever knew or cared who won the title, it was of the utmost importance to the hockey-mad natives.

The Harrisville fans loyally insisted that their team would mop up the ice with the invaders, and backed up their contention with cash bets.

The Pennifer crowd swore by all the powers of hockey that any team that could be licked by the Kingfish was all washed up and on the way out.

Toby Mackenzie wasn't any too confident of the outcome. His high-scoring forward line had gone to pieces, and he knew it. Toby made vain endeavours to get the line clicking again, worked over them in practice, begged them to settle their differences and get going as of old. And every man of the three told him the same thing.

"It isn't my fault. I can't score goals if I don't get passes."

Mackenzie tore his hair. "There'll be a different scoring system in this league next season if I have any say in it," he groaned.

The point system, with credit for assists, was not in use in the loop. Goals counted, and nothing else.

Dan Hawley was sullen and tight-lipped when he skated out for the face-off before the bellowing crowd that packed the rink for the final.

If O'Hara and Borstall didn't want to pass to him, that was fine by him. He'd earn more credit when he whipped the Owls single-handed. He glanced over at Mary, in a rail seat near the players' bench, and winked in recognition of a wave from her gloved hand. Then he squared off for the draw.

It was going to be a tough, hard game. The first period showed that. The heavy Owl defence was like a wall. The forwards were glued to their checks. There was a man riding every puck carrier. When you got past the blue line, it was *smash*, *thud* and *bang*, with skates, sticks and bodies barring the way to the cage.

For twenty minutes, the see-saw battle was scoreless. Twice Dan Hawley flashed his way through to the goal mouth, once with the puck, once creating a play that brought Steve O'Hara in with him, O'Hara carrying the disc and in the clear to lay down a pass.

The goalie outsmarted Dan on the first chance, refusing to fall for Dan's fake pass. He took the shot on his pads and sent it into the corner. And on the second chance, when Steve O'Hara shot from the angle instead of playing along with Dan on the try, the Owl goalie covered the open corner smartly and smothered the rebound.

• • •

EARLY IN THE second period, Dan had another try, a long shot that missed. And when he went in after the rebound, a defenceman cleared it. Judge, the Owl centre, snapped up the pass and bolted down the middle lane with Dan racing to overhaul him.

Judge had a good lead, however, and the Owl forwards worked a perfect triple pass at the Panther defence, a play that brought Judge and his right winger inside for a short pass and a close shot that beat the goalie cleanly. The joyous screech that went up from the Owl fans rattled the girders.

Owls, 1; Panthers, 0.

The first-string forwards took a rest, and then went out again. Toby Mackenzie's fervent plea was ringing in their ears.

"Boys, pass that puck! A little teamwork!"

They got one goal. O'Hara gave Borstall a pass from behind the Owl net, and Borstall banged it in for the Panthers' first tally. But the Owls countered twice.

Dan Hawley never displayed better speed and stick-handling than in that second frame. His swift, dazzling thrusts riddled the Owl front line. He swooped in on the defence time and again, stickhandling sensationally, electrifying the crowd with his rushes.

Half a dozen times, he tore in alone; twice, he yanked the crowd to its feet with rushes right through the entire Owl team, from goal to goal. Judge couldn't hold him. The Owl defencemen got the jitters every time they saw him coming. But he couldn't score.

Dan did everything but get the puck into the net. It was heartbreaking, bewildering to the crowd, maddening to Dan. He was playing the game of his life, keeping the play up in the Owl zone two-thirds of the time, sending the crowd frantic with his dazzling attacks, but he couldn't get that rubber over the goal line.

Always, at the last minute, something happened. A defenceman knocked him off stride; he couldn't get set for a hard shot; he was forced to shoot from a bad angle; a stick or an arm intercepted the puck; the goalie blocked; the puck hit the post. Always something.

The Owls had a two-goal lead that looked as big as a mountain, and they were hanging on to it tenaciously.

The Panthers, forced to carry the play and take big chances, were lagging when the period came to an end.

Dan stumbled off the ice on skates that seemed made of lead. His body sagged with exhaustion. In the dressing room he sprawled on the rubbing table while the trainer slammed and pummelled his aching muscles. As if from a long distance away he heard the hubbub of voices around him.

"We'll take 'em yet . . ."

"That goalie is tough . . ."

"I smacked that left winger so hard I'll bet his forty-second cousin felt it . . ."

"Two goals to tie and three to win for us . . ."

And then, he heard one of the club officials who had crowded into the dressing room: "Boy, isn't Dan playing a whale of a game? I never saw such tough luck as he had that period."

Toby Mackenzie answered: "They're all playing a great game. Every man of 'em. But the team is punk!"

Dan sat up. Toby Mackenzie met his eye. There was a challenge in the hard blue glance.

• • •

DAN WAS THINKING hard when the third period got under way. He snapped up the loose puck when an Owl attack broke at the defence, circled the net, getting up speed for a rush.

They were all playing a great game. He was playing a great game. But just the same, they were two goals down and on their way to a licking that would cost them the title—because the team was punk!

You couldn't fool Toby Mackenzie. He knew. And it came to Dan, as he rounded the net and hit toward the middle lane, that the coach had put his finger on the weakness. The players were good. But the team itself wasn't good enough. And Mackenzie's hard, accusing stare told him who was to blame.

Dan hit mid-ice, stickhandled his way past Judge, swooped down on the blue line. What did it matter who scored the goals as long as the goals were scored? He tore across the line, skates flashing, the roar of the crowd booming in his ears.

Maybe a solo goal looked swell to the crowd, but it wasn't good hockey if you failed to make it after failing to cinch the counter by passing to a teammate who had a better chance.

Dan Hawley headed straight for the defence. They closed in to sandwich him. He hadn't fed a pass to either wing all evening. Dan waited until the last split second, then whipped the puck across to O'Hara on the wing.

The pass was a little slow reaching O'Hara's stick. He fumbled it for a second. But he got his shot away. The puck zipped past the goalie and sent the Panther fans into seventh heaven.

One goal to tie and two to win. The Panthers were flying now. That goal seemed to lift the whole team. They smashed in on the attack again, swept in for another rush that was broken up at the defence. The Owls hit back, were staved off. The stumbling forwards were relieved.

Back came the first stringers. Dan Hawley snagged the puck near the Owl blue line, strode in, fired from outside the defence.

It missed the net, but Dan was already hurtling through after it. He snatched it, as it caromed across the ice, came in swiftly from the side. The goalie pulled over, a defenceman lunged toward him.

A short, sharp pass to O'Hara's stick. O'Hara stepped in, faked a shot, drilled the puck over to Borstall. The puck went like a bullet from Borstall's stick into the back of the cage.

The crowd went mad. The Owls, frantic now, went on the attack. The Panther forwards checked them to a standstill; checked hard and furiously, until Dan saw an opening. He snapped up the puck and raced through, with O'Hara and Borstall flying abreast of him.

They bunched as they hit the defence. The puck snapped from stick to stick so quickly that the crowd could scarcely follow it. The old, short-passing game.

O'Hara was through with the puck, and Dan Hawley was with him. In they raced, with the crowd gone mad. A pass to Dan, he pulled over, and the goalie moved.

Here, if ever, was the greatest temptation of his life. Steve had given him that pass and he was right on top of the goalie, almost in the crease. He had a glorious opportunity to score the goal that would bring Harrisville the title. Dan's wrists tensed, the goalie crouched, lunged . . .

And Dan snapped the puck back to Steve O'Hara, who socked it into the open side of the net for the clincher.

• • •

DAN HAWLEY DIDN'T even know that Paddy Garner had been at the game until the Redmen's scout talked to him afterward. Their conversation didn't last long, but it meant plenty to Dan.

"I watched you in another game this winter," said Garner, "but I put you down as a puck hog. A grandstander, see! But I thought I'd come back for another look, just to see if I was wrong, because I liked your style. And for a while tonight, Hawley, I thought my first guess was the right one. But that third-period rampage of yours proved different. How about coming down to the Redmen next season? We need a play-maker like you. We have lots of boys who can slap the puck into the net when the play is set up for them, but the fellows who can set it up are as scarce as hen's teeth."

"I guess we can talk business, Mister Garner. I figure on getting married."

"Is your girl a hockey fan?" chuckled Garner.

"Sure. But she doesn't know a whole lot about the game," answered Dan Hawley.

ABOUT LESLIE McFARLANE

To young detectives worldwide, Leslie McFarlane was known under the pseudonyms Carolyn Keene, Roy Rockwood and, most famously, Franklin W. Dixon—author of The Hardy Boys series. McFarlane, who passed away in 1977, was one of the most successful Canadian writers of all time. Working for the *Stratemeyer Syndicate*, he penned 21 volumes of The Hardy Boys, initiated The Dana Girls series and wrote seven Dave Fearless novels. Aside from his work as The Hardy Boys author, McFarlane penned four novels, 100 novelettes, 200 short stories, and 75 television scripts. He also produced, directed and wrote 50 films for the National Film Board. McFarlane was nominated for an Academy Award for scripting the documentary drama *Herring Hunt* in 1953. He also worked in Hollywood as a writer for the television show *Bonanza* before returning to Canada where he worked on documentaries and comedies for the CBC. He passed away in 1977, at the age of 75.